Molecular Biology

Molecular Biology

ELEMENTARY PROCESSES OF
NERVE CONDUCTION AND MUSCLE CONTRACTION

Edited by DAVID NACHMANSOHN

A symposium sponsored by Columbia University and The Rockefeller Institute; held at The Rockefeller Institute from September 25th to 30th, 1958

1960

ACADEMIC PRESS • *New York and London*

ACADEMIC PRESS INC.
111 FIFTH AVENUE
NEW YORK 3, N. Y.

United Kingdom Edition
Published by
ACADEMIC PRESS INC. (LONDON) LTD.
17 OLD QUEEN STREET, LONDON S.W. 1

Library of Congress Catalog Card Number 59-15758

PRINTED IN THE UNITED STATES OF AMERICA

Participants in
the Symposium on Molecular Biology

Lord Adrian
Frank Brink, Jr.
Detlev W. Bronk
Fritz Buchthal
Carlos Chagas
Anne Chain
Ernst Chain
Britton Chance
Sze-chuh Cheng
K. S. Cole
Clarence M. Connelly
William V. Consolazio
Rene Couteaux
Arpad I. Csapo
R. E. Davies
Peter Debye
Wolf Dettbarn
Vincent P. Dole, Jr.
Vincent du Vigneaud
J. C. Eccles
John T. Edsall
Seymour Ehrenpreis
Henry Eyring
Jordi Folch-Pi
Herbert S. Gasser
M. Guinnebault
H. Keffer Hartline
A. V. Hill
William P. Hurlbut
A. F. Huxley
Hugh Huxley

Herbert Jasper
R. D. Keynes
John G. Kirkwood
Hans A. Krebs
K. S. Krishnan
S. W. Kuffler
Polykarp Kusch
Fritz A. Lipmann
David P. C. Lloyd
Lewis G. Longsworth
Rafael Lorente de Nó
Barbara Low
Werner Lowenstein
Duncan A. MacInnes
Karl Meyer
Stanley Miller
A. M. Monnier
Manuel F. Morales
David Nachmansohn
William Nastuk
Severo Ochoa
Gertrude E. Perlmann
David Robertson
H. Scheraga
Ernest Schoffeniels
Theodore Shedlovsky
J. Shulman
Robert Staempfli
George Wald
Hans H. Weber
Irwin B. Wilson

Yngve Zotterman

Contents

Contents

Introductory Remarks

DETLEV W. BRONK

President of The Rockefeller Institute

It is my pleasant privilege to extend the welcome of The Rockefeller Institute and the National Science Foundation to so many of our friends and colleagues from so many other countries, as well as other institutions. Dr. Nachmansohn will, I am sure, wish to extend similar greetings from Columbia University.

We are all of us in this country grateful to you for having come so far to share with us your friendship and your knowledge. If we can make your visit intellectually profitable and socially pleasant, it will be a very small symbol of our great gratitude for your hospitality and friendship of other years in other places, for the inspiration of ideals that we hold in common, for the benefit of shared knowledge. This company in a very personal way evokes for me happy memories spread over three happy decades. They began just thirty years ago this year in the laboratories and in the company of Adrian and Hill. And for me it is a very special and a moving privilege to have them here in this institution which is beginning a new era. Through them I came to know Sherrington, Lapicque and many others who are known to you and who have meant so much to us in the past development of our science. To them I am also deeply indebted for the opportunity they provided to begin the building of a scientific life which has included the friendship and association with most of you who are here assembled. I speak of this not as a prelude to the history of our subject which you and they and their predecessors have built. Those achievements will be implicit in the communications which follow. Our motives, our unity of effort and the significance of our achievements are, however, worthy of further interpretation which I would like to take just a few minutes to develop even though it may seem to have no place in a discussion which is to be informal and focused on a very special field of science. But I think that a gathering of friends such as this has a special significance in these times of trial, tribulation, and potential triumph of the human mind, which is, however, greatly threatened. I think if there was ever a time in the history of the modern world when there is need for friendship, it is now, and I think that such a gathering as this illustrates in a very meaningful way the capacity of men to live together in sincerity and to work for a better way of life which includes the creative efforts rather than the destruction of so much that is good that has come before. And so, as I say, I know that you will forgive me if I try to give a broader interpretation than the mere scientific development of our ideas, if I speak of what seems to me to be so meaningful a thing as the gathering together of those of us who have come together here and who have spent so much time in the past working and playing together without regard for national boundaries or limited ideologies. I wish I had the power to put in adequately expressive words the especial reasons why the friendly associations of international gatherings such as this give to those of us who are Americans so much pleasure. It is in part, I think, because we are so recently come from your native lands. Our nation has been made by those who are brothers of your fathers. Your ancestors were our ancestors too. Our feeling of friendly kinship is due in part, I further think, to our common cultural heritage. The first visit of an American to your several countries is a remarkable experience. Before it one has the bewildering feeling, if I can interpret your feelings in terms of mine, the bewildering feeling that one has seen it all before. And so one has, through the eyes and words of those who wrote the literature of your country which was the literature of our fathers on which we, too, were reared. Another deeply rooted reason for our feeling of close association with you is the recent growth of science in this country from the seeds brought by our teachers who first studied in your lands, as we who had the benefit of working with you in your laboratories are trying to plant the seeds in the minds and spirit of our students and younger colleagues. It is significant to remember at a time when diplomats are not always motivated by the friendly spirit of true scientists and at a time when science is increasingly being used as an instrument of political propaganda and conflict between nations that Benjamin Franklin, our first great diplomat was encouraged by election to the Royal Society of London, the Royal Academy of Sciences at Goettingen, academies of science at Paris, Padua, and St. Petersburg. From those days of Franklin until now we have a deep debt of gratitude to you for first nurturing those who then developed science here. And so I say our warm welcome has natural roots and traditions and brotherly associations which we hope you of our mother countries may understand. And so I say again that in these times when some of us cannot escape the daily consciousness of impending catastrophe and, yes, disaster because there are not enough who are willing to associate in friendship as we are that we may take just a moment as we begin these days of friendly meeting to recall that we can do more than further science and apply science as an instrument to a better way of life. We can help to make a more peaceful way of life which will lead to a better way of life. We will represent to many others what we have found it possible to do. In these gatherings then, today, and in the days to come I hope that we may demonstrate the spirit of friendship which is not always present even within our several countries, friendship based on frankness and willingness to discuss our ideas and divergence of opinion. And having said that I go on to a more practical consideration and that is the remark of George Wald just made to me a moment ago in which he said that the real reason for coming together is to have such a body as this meeting together for some days and for frank discussion. He went so far as to say that he hoped that I would encourage you to interrupt the speakers, let alone discuss their papers at the end, if there were points which you do not understand as they proceed. I know that you will do this in orderly fashion and I think that George had an important point in beginning at the beginning to develop the spirit of discussion which is the purpose of this small gathering of those of us who have worked in the various fields in the furtherance of our common field. But it would be better for me to let the aims of the Symposium be described by David Nachmansohn who has been the initiator of this conference, its constant stimulus and to whom we are all indebted.

The Aims of the Symposium

David Nachmansohn

The eloquent and moving words of welcome by President Bronk have admirably expressed the spirit in which this Symposium was organized and the deep feelings of friendship prevailing at present among the scientists of the Western world, transcending all boundaries. Our ardent hope is, in spite of situations and events that are sometimes frightening, that the scientific community will eventually encompass the whole civilized world.

A few remarks appear appropriate about the aim of this Symposium, the ideas which formed the basis of its organization. The startling developments which have taken place in physics since the turn of this century have had a strong impact on science in general. First, they have deeply affected all scientific thinking and philosophy. Classical physics based on Newton's mechanics led scientists to believe that their concepts were a direct result of observation and experimental data and that the laws proposed were necessarily derived from their findings. Certain concepts and notions were considered as undisputable and final truths; any change was opposed with a rather rigid frame of mind. One of the results of the achievements of modern physics has been the realization, emphasized particularly by Einstein, but also by many others, that the physical scientist arrives at his theory only indirectly by speculative means. Without going into the ever more complex philosophical problems raised by the quantum theory, especially the Heisenberg principle of indeterminacy, it is apparent that we are faced in modern physics with the existence of different closed and coherent sets of systems, concepts with a limited applicability which sometimes result in paradoxical answers to a special question. The analysis and the understanding of experimental data and of new phenomena frequently cannot be achieved by the use of known concepts and established laws, but require entirely new notions and theories. The limited range of applicability of every concept is one of the most important lessons learned.

If facts and experimental data alone are inadequate for formulating a theory or a concept, if our knowledge is based not purely on observation and experiment but depends largely on the underlying theory, it follows that any concept is of necessity bound to be subjected to profound modifications and corrections. The appearance of new evidence incompatible with previous assumptions and theories, no matter how well established they may have appeared to be for long periods of time, makes necessary a readjustment of existing notions. Scientific attitude toward pronouncements of theories and concepts can, therefore, not accept the claim of certainty but only of probability on the basis of present evidence.

Another outcome of the progress of physics and chemistry is the availability of extremely powerful tools for biological sciences. These new tools have made possible extraordinary and fascinating progress in our understanding of mechanisms of living cells in terms of physics and chemistry far beyond anything which was possible to foresee or to imagine at the beginning of this century. In some fields the advances have reached molecular levels. The question raised by many philosophers and scientists in the past, namely whether we are able to explain events in a living cell taking place at a given time and in a given space in terms of physics and chemistry, was discussed by Schroedinger in his essays: "What is Life?". Schroedinger admits that we have not yet reached the stage where we can explain life phenomena on the molecular level, but he considers the progress made as an indication that it will eventually become possible. Although the assumption of "vital" forces still discussed some thirty years ago has been generally abandoned today, the optimistic attitude of Schroedinger is not shared by all. There are certain aspects of living cells for which many scientists would be reluctant to accept the view that physics and chemistry will be able to provide the final answer. This applies for instance to certain functions of the brain such as the working of the human mind: the problems of thinking, of psychology, of emotions, of ethics, and others. These phenomena belong in a different category in the definition of Kant.

But many aspects of living cells are open to physicochemical analysis. However, the extraordinary complexity of living cells presents formidable obstacles. The last few decades have seen great advances in the investigations of structure and ultra-structure, of physical manifestations and chemical processes underlying cellular function. But perhaps due to the rapidity of the progress in special fields the integration of the new knowledge has become difficult and is far from satisfactory. Here the danger of rigidly maintaining traditional concepts becomes obvious. New fresh ideas, on the other hand, may open new ways and greatly stimulate an entire field. If it is true that even in physics no definitely established concepts and notions exist; if, for instance, the theory of relativity has changed such fundamental concepts as space and time and other seemingly solidly established philosophical and scientific notions, then all the more should the biologist be aware of how uncertain his concepts must be at present. Clearly, it is absolutely essential for real progress to keep the mind open for entirely new ideas and concepts in a field that, due to its complexity, is still far behind physics and chemistry as to the level of precision and insight.

The conference differs from the usual pattern of bringing together active and competent investigators of a special field and providing them with an opportunity to present and review the available information. The aim of this Symposium is that of emphasizing the discussion of fundamental concepts and notions by a group of scientists of a widely different background but all interested in the basic problem of what is widely referred to as Molecular Biology. As James B. Conant stressed in his lectures on "Modern Science and Modern Man," the essential element in the advance of modern science has been the interplay between theoretical notion and the experiment of the specialist. "The history of science," he writes, "demonstrates beyond doubt that the really revolutionary and significant advances came not from empiricism alone but from new theories. The development of these theories, in turn, has depended on free discussion of their consequences." Indeed, many examples may be quoted where most fruitful developments took place when different types of thinking met.

It was felt that new types of approach and new ideas might be stimulated and certain notions and concepts clarified by bringing together physicists and chemists with a group of biologists working on different lines and with different methods, i.e. either on ultrastructure or on the chemistry or on the physical events of living cells. Two topics were selected about which much information has accumulated as to the underlying elementary processes: muscular contraction and nerve impulse conduction. Only a relatively small number of papers will be presented in order to formulate problems and to provide a factual basis for a fruitful discussion.

In order to promote a really informal, intensive and fruitful exchange of ideas the Organizing Committee considered it imperative to limit the participants to a small number. The Committee, therefore, had the unhappy duty of making a somewhat arbitrary choice in selecting participants among the great number of investigators who are competent and interested in these problems.

Although the material presented covers only a few aspects of a variety of fields, the high quality of the papers and the wealth of important new information and new ideas made it appear desirable to combine them in a special volume.

The hospitality of President Bronk who made available the facilities of the Aldrich Hall of the Rockefeller Institute with its gracious atmosphere was greatly appreciated by all participants. The Editor would like to express his personal indebtedness to the President and his associates for their active participation and valuable advice and help in organizing this Symposium. The conference was made possible by a generous grant from the National Science Foundation.

The Structure of Striated Muscle

HUGH E. HUXLEY

*Medical Research Council, Department of Biophysics,
University College London, England*

The phenomenon of muscular contraction has been studied in great detail, and with considerable success, by the classic disciplines of physiology and biochemistry, the one concerned with the macroscopic properties and behavior of muscles, the other with the chemical reactions taking place during the various phases of muscular activity. A well-established picture of many aspects of the contractile process, as seen from these two points of view, is now available, but it is a picture with a very large gap in it, for the causal link between the chemical reactions and the contraction to which they give rise is not known. That is, we do not yet know what exactly are the structural changes at the molecular level which occur as a consequence or an accompaniment of the chemical reactions taking place during contraction, and the process by which those molecular changes are summated to produce macroscopic shortening is only partially understood. However, information concerning the submicroscopic structure of striated muscle offers the possibility of establishing definite relationships between the two different approaches to the subject, so that eventually the detailed physiological observations can be translated into their implications in terms of events at the molecular level, and the physiological consequences of particular chemical events can become calculable. Let us see how far we can take this process at present.

THE DEVELOPMENT OF THE "SLIDING FILAMENT" HYPOTHESIS

The structural evidence seems to favor very strongly the "interdigitating filament" or "double array" model of striated muscle (Hanson and H. E. Huxley, 1953), and contraction seems to be brought about by a process in which the two arrays of filaments in each sarcomere are made to slide past each other (A. F. Huxley and Niedergerke, 1954; H. E. Huxley and Hanson,

1954). I will describe the main pieces of evidence which have
led to this view, and then discuss very briefly some relationships between various phenomena in muscle on which the structural information throws a little new light.

The earliest electron microscope studies on muscle (Hall et al.,
1946; Draper and Hodge, 1949) had shown that the myofibrils
of striated muscle contained longitudinal filaments about 100 A
or so in diameter, which remained relatively straight and well
oriented even after contraction. They also showed clearly that
the characteristic band pattern arose from a well-defined variation in density along the length of the fibrils. The precise way
in which the filaments were arranged *in vivo*, and in particular
their lateral arrangement, could not readily be ascertained at
that time, for the only technique available was one in which
isolated myofibrils, prepared by mechanically fragmenting the
whole muscle, were dried down into the electron microscope
grids.

X-Ray Observations

The first indications that the contractile material of striated
muscle was built up from two sets of filaments came from low-
angle X-ray diffraction studies on muscle examined in the wet
state, both under normal physiological conditions and in a state
of rigor (H. E. Huxley, 1952, 1953a). Such muscles give a characteristic and well-defined X-ray pattern; the equatorial reflections reveal the presence of a regular hexagonal array of filaments spaced out about 450 A apart and obviously corresponding
to the filaments seen in the earlier micrographs. It became clear
that these filaments formed a more or less continuous array
across each myofibril and were not located around the periphery
alone, as had sometimes been supposed. The space between the
filaments would of course be occupied by sarcoplasm.

In muscle in rigor, the hexagonal array still appeared to be
present, but the intensities of the X-ray reflection differed from
those given by living muscle in a manner which suggested that
a secondary array of filaments had now become fixed in position
at the trigonal points of the lattice, i.e., at the points lying symmetrically between three of the original "primary" filaments.

As the onset of rigor was known to be associated with the disappearance of adenosine triphosphate (ATP) from the muscle, and as the absence of ATP would allow combination between actin and myosin to take place, it was suggested that these two principal structural proteins were localized in the two separate sets of filaments; that the secondary filaments were fairly randomly arranged among the array of primary ones in living muscle containing ATP; and that in rigor the secondary filaments became attached at specific sites in the array by the formation of actin-myosin linkages, thus giving rise to the observed changes in X-ray pattern. The available evidence did not make it possible to decide which protein was contained in which set of filaments, nor did it of course provide any evidence or indication about localization of those proteins in particular regions of the sarcomere, except that it required them to be present together in some regions at least. However, it was found that living muscle gave a very sharp set of axial reflections corresponding to a 415 A axial periodicity, which remained unaltered when the muscle was stretched and which, so far as could be judged from the rather poor patterns given by contracted muscle, was not changed by shortening either.

Confirmation of the "Double Array" Theory

The development of the technique of ultrathin sectioning of tissue for the electron microscope made it possible to take the structural studies several stages further. It was confirmed that the myofilaments were arranged in hexagonal fashion across the myofibrils (Bennett and Porter, 1953; Hodge et al., 1954), a result also indicated by some very early observations on thin sections (Morgan et al., 1950); and the presence of the double array of filaments was confirmed by more detailed studies of cross sections of muscle taken through various bands of the sarcomere (H. E. Huxley, 1953b). These showed, in the A-bands, a very regular hexagonal array of thicker filaments about 100 A in diameter, with thinner filaments, about 50 A in diameter, lying symmetrically at the expected positions in between them (see Fig. 1). No such double array could be detected in the

I-bands however, which at that time were usually rather badly preserved but which only seemed to show thin filaments.

This was a puzzling result at first, but the reason for it became apparent when it was found that the high optical density and birefringence of the A-bands disappeared when muscle was treated with solvents (high ionic strength salt solutions plus ATP or pyrophosphate) known to dissolve out myosin selectively (Hanson and H. E. Huxley, 1953; Hasselbach, 1953).

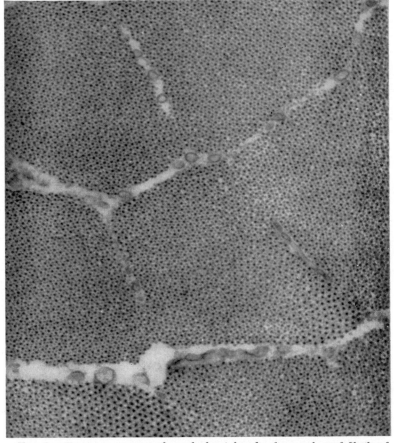

Fig. 1. Transverse section through the A-bands of a number of fibrils of rabbit psoas muscle showing double hexagonal array of large and small filaments, cut end-on. Magnification: × 50,000.

Moreover, electron micrographs of muscle which had been treated in this fashion showed that the larger filaments were no longer present, and that only thin filaments remained; the distinction between A- and I-bands had disappeared.

It was, therefore, natural to suggest that the myosin in the muscle was contained in the array of thicker filaments in the A-bands (each filament being continuous from one end of the A-band to the other), and that the presence of this array of myosin filaments was responsible for the high density and bire-fringence of the A-bands. The protein actin, on the other hand, was assigned to the thinner filaments, extending from the Z-lines, through the I-bands, into the A-bands, where they lay in between the myosin filaments, up to the H-zone, where they terminated. No thin filaments could be seen in cross sections through the H-zone (Fig. 2), although the thicker ones were still

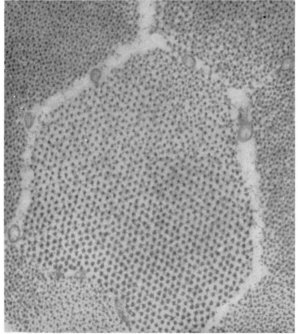

Fig. 2.   Transverse section through the H-zone of a psoas fibril, showing simple hexagonal array of large filaments.

present, and their absence from this region would account for the characteristic lower density there. This interdigitating filament model of striated muscle is illustrated in Fig. 3, and the ideas embodied in it have been considerably strengthened and extended by subsequent experiments.

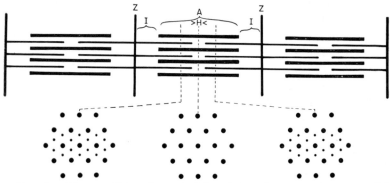

FIG. 3. Diagram illustrating principles of interdigitating filament model of striated muscle. Upper portion shows three successive sarcomeres with their interpenetrating arrays of filaments. Lower portion shows end-on view of structure at different points in the sarcomere.

FURTHER EVIDENCE CONCERNING THE LOCALIZATION OF ACTIN AND MYOSIN

The localization of myosin in the A-bands, originally postulated on purely qualitative grounds, has been confirmed by quantitative measurements, made in the interference microscope, of the relative amounts of protein present in the different regions of the sarcomere, and of the amounts removed during myosin extraction (H. E. Huxley and Hanson, 1957; Hanson and H. E. Huxley, 1957). These showed that about 54.5% of all the protein in isolated well-washed myofibrils was present as the "extra" material in the A-bands, i.e., as material which raised the density of the A-bands above the level of the I-bands and hence corresponded to the array of thick filaments, present only in the A-bands. When myosin extraction was performed, all this extra material was removed, together with about 10% of the total fibrillar protein which was extracted from the regions of the sarcomere occupied by the thinner filaments.

Biochemical studies on identical preparations of myofibrils showed that the extracted myosin made up 50-55% of the total protein of the myofibrils, and that the extracts also contained some other unidentified protein or proteins amounting to about 10% of the original total protein. These results showed that at least 4/5 of the myosin *must* be located in the A-bands, and they were in complete agreement with the idea that all the myosin was located there, and that the other protein removed along with the myosin came from the thinner filaments.

More recently, Corsi and Perry (1958) have shown that certain treatments which completely dissolve out the I-bands of isolated myofibrils do not result in any myosin appearing in the extract; and all the ATPase activity of the fibrils (myofibrillar ATPase being specifically associated with myosin) remains behind in the residue of A-segments. Further, the extract contained tropomyosin and what appeared to be a denatured form of actin, always present in roughly the same proportions, suggesting that the two proteins were associated together in the thin filaments.

The conclusion that myosin is located in the thick filaments in the A-bands, and that actin is located in the thin filaments in both A- and I-bands, thus seems to be rather well established.

FURTHER ELECTRON MICROSCOPE OBSERVATIONS

The structural arrangements present in muscle have been investigated in greater detail in the electron microscope recently, using improved instrument and specimen techniques (H. E. Huxley, 1957). In particular, the use of much thinner sections to avoid the confusion owing to superposition of different structures within the thickness of the section, and the use of phosphotungstic acid (PTA) dissolved in absolute alcohol as an electron stain giving high contrast, have greatly extended the range of useful information obtainable. Using these two techniques together, it is possible to see the two types of filaments, lying alongside each other, in suitably oriented longitudinal sections of striated muscle, and the appearance of such sections is illustrated in Fig. 4. In these sections, which only contain one filament within the thickness of the section (∼ 150 A), pairs of thin filaments are seen between adjacent thick ones; this effect is a consequence of the geometry of the double hexagonal lattice, as can be seen from Fig. 5.

Imperfections in the orientation and linearity of the filaments in the I-bands and at the A–I boundary make it impossible to trace each thin filament all the way from the H-zone to the Z-line, but counts of filaments made on serial cross sections show that the number of filaments in the I-band of a given fibril is equal to the number of *thin* filaments in the adjoining A-band

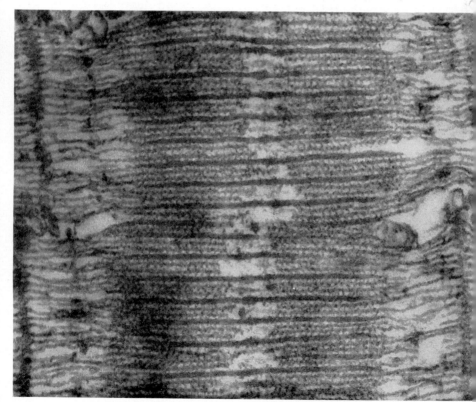

Fig. 4. Very thin longitudinal section of striated muscle showing large and small filaments lying side by side and connected together by system of cross bridges. Note absence of thin filaments from H-zone, and absence of thick filaments from I-band. Magnification: × 120,000.

of the same fibril. As there are only half as many thick filaments in the lattice as there are thin ones, this observation is very difficult to reconcile with any conclusion other than that the thick filaments terminate completely at the ends of the A-band (as indeed they often appear to do), and that the thin filaments continue on up to the Z-lines.

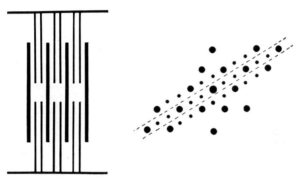

Fig. 5.   Diagram illustrating how characteristic appearance of filaments in ultrathin (∼ 150 A) longitudinal sections arises from geometry of double hexagonal lattice. The dotted line indicates the profile of the region contained in the longitudinal section.

Another characteristic feature of the structure which can be seen very clearly in the ultrathin longitudinal sections is a system of cross bridges which seem to provide lateral connection between the thick and the thin filaments. These bridges, which are also visible in the transverse sections, occur at approximately 400 A intervals along the length of the muscle between each adjacent thick and thin filament. As each thick filament has six thin ones around it, six such bridges occur every 400 A along the thick filaments, and so far as can be seen, they are spaced out at regular intervals of 60–70 A. The attachments to a given thin filament from the three thick ones around it do not occur in register either, but occur at intervals of 130–140 A. The appearance in longitudinal sections of bridges between adjacent thin filaments is an artifact; these are in fact bridges to thick filaments above and below the plane of the section, as can be seen from cross sections. The bridges seem to form a permanent part of the thick filaments, for under conditions, which we will describe later, where the thin filaments are partly withdrawn from the array of thick ones, the bridges remain, projecting out sideways from the thick filaments, in the region of the A-band from which the thin filaments are now absent.

Each thick filament, then, has approximately 210 to 230 cross bridges projecting from it, and it can be calculated that there are approximately 5×10^{16} such bridges in one gram of muscle It is interesting to note that this quantity of muscle contains, on present biochemical estimates, approximately 10×10^{16} molecules of myosin. The close similarity between these two numbers, derived from such widely different kinds of observation, is rather striking, and tempts one to suggest that each bridge is associated with one or two myosin molecules, and perhaps represents a portion of that part of the myosin molecule, H-meromyosin (A. G. Szent-Györgyi, 1953), which possesses the ability to combine with actin and to split ATP.

CHANGES IN STRUCTURE DURING CONTRACTION AND STRETCH

We shall now consider what changes take place in these overlapping arrays of filaments when the muscle contracts, or when it is passively stretched. We have already seen that the band pattern of striated muscle is a direct manifestation, which we can observe in the light microscope, of the way in which the filaments are arranged; and so by finding out how this band pattern is altered by changes in muscle length and by changes in the state of activity of the muscle, we should be able to tell a good deal about how the filaments themselves are behaving.

Rather conflicting accounts of band pattern changes have appeared in the literature during the last eighty years, and it is only with the introduction of the phase contrast and interference microscopes that observations which do not contain a considerable subjective element have become possible. A. F. Huxley and Niedergerke (1954) have used the interference microscope to investigate the band pattern changes in living muscle fibers during physiological contractions and during stretch, and the present author and Dr. Jean Hanson (H. E. Huxley and Hanson, 1954) have used the phase contrast microscope to make observations on isolated myofibrils, contracting in ATP solutions or being stretched under various conditions. In the latter experiments, myosin extraction was carried out at various stages of contraction and stretch so as to reveal more clearly the position of the actin filaments.

In each case, it was found that the length of the A-bands remained approximately constant, both during stretch and during moderate degrees of contraction, and the changes in sarcomere length were accounted for solely by changes in length of the I-bands. When shortening to below 60–70% rest length (R.L.) occurred, the I-bands disappeared altogether, and dark bands (contraction bands) appeared where adjacent A-bands came into apposition at the Z-lines, as though the thick filaments were being crumpled up in this region. It was also found that the length of the H-zone (the lighter region in the center of the A-band) varied with sarcomere length, being longer in stretched muscle, and disappearing and being replaced by a dark line or band below about 85% R.L. The distance from the Z-line to the edge of the H-zone remained approximately constant down to the point where the H-zone disappeared.

Since the length of the A-bands is equal to the length of the thick (myosin) filaments, and since the distance from the Z-line to the edge of the H-zone is equal to the length of the thin (actin) filaments, it follows from the observations that the lengths of both types of filament must remain approximately constant over a wide range of muscle lengths, and that changes in muscle length, whether active or passive, must be brought about by a process in which the two sets of filaments slide past each other.

Implications of the Sliding Filament Hypothesis

The idea that the filaments slide without changing their length provides an immediate explanation for the constancy of the 400 A axial X-ray spacing, for whether it is due to periodicities in the actin or in the myosin filaments or in both, it should remain unchanged after changes in muscle length. The idea also provides a simple explanation for the characteristically large decrease in the extensibility of a muscle when it passes into rigor, a change associated with the disappearance of ATP from the muscle. It has already been argued that this change would lead to the formation of cross linkages between the actin and the myosin filaments. In the absence of such linkages, as in living, resting muscle containing ATP which is not being split, the two sets of filaments should be able to slide past each other relatively freely; in the presence of permanent cross linkages the sliding movement would be inhibited and the extensibility of the muscle greatly reduced.

Following this line of thought, it is also natural to suppose that the cross bridges are involved rather directly in producing the sliding movement in actively contracting muscle, in which ATP (or some other high-energy phosphate compound) is being split. How they could do this is of course the most interesting and important problem that we have to solve, and there is at present remarkably little experimental evidence to assist us. There are, however, one or two features of such a process upon which one might usefully comment.

In the first place, the range of movement in an axial direction of the distal ends of each cross bridge is likely to be rather limited, and indeed electron micrographs of muscle, even at widely different lengths, show only slight variations in the tilt and the separation of the bridges. Even if each bridge could move in an axial direction by an amount equal to the axial separation of the observed attachment points on the actin filaments ($\sim$ 130 A), and if it could draw the actin filament along as it did so, the amount of shortening produced would only be about 1% of the muscle length. For such a process to generate substantial amounts of shortening it must be repetitive, i.e., each cross bridge must be able to change its point of attachment to the actin filament and repeat the "pulling" process a number of times each time the muscle shortens. One therefore forms a picture in which the cross bridges are all continually going through cycles of interaction with the attachment points on the actin filaments moving past them as the muscle contracts.

The tension generated will depend on the number of cross bridges attached at any given moment to the actin filaments. When the velocity of shortening of a muscle is high, the tension observed is small; this effect, which is not due to internal viscosity, is readily explicable if some step in the reactions at the cross bridges limits the rate at which attachment can take place between a "free" bridge and a particular actin site moving past it. A detailed scheme of this general nature has been described by A. F. Huxley (1957) and shown to give very satisfactory agreement with experiment.

It is natural to suppose that the breakdown of some energy-rich phosphate compound is involved in the tension generation at the cross bridges. If one assumes that one such molecule is split, liberating 10,000 calories per mole, each time one cross bridge goes through one cycle of its operation, and if one assumes that each bridge can generate tension once every time the neighboring actin filament moves along 130 A, then it is easy to show that the maximum tension exerted by the muscle would be of the order of 3–4 kg per square centimeter. This is in good agreement with observed values, so that one can say that such a mechanism is at the very least quantitatively practicable.

To account for the observed *rate* of energy liberation by typical striated muscles, the cross bridges would need to act at rates up to 30–100 times per second. These figures do not seem unduly high compared with the turnover rates of other enzymatic reactions.

Another very important and interesting characteristic of striated muscle is its ability to vary the amount of energy released during a contraction according to the amount of external work performed. Some of the energy released always appears as heat— part of it as a fairly constant "heat of activation" which appears whether the muscle is allowed to shorten or not, part of it as "heat of shortening" which is liberated in proportion to the amount of shortening taking place and is independent of the load which the muscle is lifting (Hill, 1938, 1949). The rest of the energy released will be equal to the amount of external work performed and so will increase with bigger loads and greater distances of shortening. Thus the total energy released, and hence the amount of chemical reaction which takes place, will increase when the muscle is allowed to shorten during a contraction, and it will have a higher value when the muscle is shortening against a large load than when it is shortening the same amount against a small one. In other words, the muscle does *not* release a fixed amount of energy each time it is stimulated, and merely vary the way that energy is divided between heat and work, but instead releases more energy when more external work is performed.

In terms of the contractile structure which we have been discussing, this means that not only does the splitting of a molecule of energy-rich phosphate *enable* a "pull" to be exerted by a cross bridge, but it means also that *unless* the cross bridge exerts a pull and does external work, the splitting of the phosphate takes place much more slowly.

There are a number of ways in which this could come about; perhaps the easiest one to imagine is where the act of attachment of a cross bridge to the actin filament activates the enzymatic splitting of the phosphate compound, and where the act of detachment, probably associated with the capture of another substrate molecule by the enzyme site, takes place much more readily when the cross bridge has drawn the actin filament along by the appropriate amount.

The existence of some such process is also indicated very strongly by certain biochemical observations. It is found that pure myosin, under the ionic conditions believed to obtain inside a muscle fiber, splits ATP only rather slowly; however, if actin is present as well, still under the same ionic conditions (where actin and myosin would be expected to combine), the splitting rate is greatly increased (e.g., Hasselbach, 1952). On the other hand, at high ionic strengths, where combination between actin and myosin is largely prevented, no activation of the myosin ATPase by actin occurs. Thus it seems that it is the *combination* of actin and myosin which makes it possible for ATP splitting to take place rapidly; though of course from this evidence alone we are not able to say which step—attachment of substrate, splitting, or removal of reaction products—is accelerated by the presence of actin.

So far, it has been convenient to think of the sliding process as one in which the actin filaments play a rather passive role, from a mechanical point of view, being merely drawn along as a result of a change in position of the cross bridges attached to them. There are certain facts, however, which make one wonder whether structural changes in the actin filaments themselves may not play a part in contraction.

Actin seems to exist in three different forms—as monomers (molecular weight 70,000), as dimers, and as long polymers (F-actin). Presumably the actin filaments in muscle contain polymerized actin. Now unpolymerized actin contains bound ATP, and when polymerization takes place, the ATP is dephosphorylated to adenosine diphosphate (ADP) (Straub and Feuer, 1950). Secondly, when actin dimers or polymers combine with myosin, there are some indications (Tsao, 1953) that they are split instantaneously into monomers. These indications were obtained from measurements of the degree of depolarization of fluorescent radiation from dye molecules attached to the actin, and there is no time here to describe these experiments (which revealed some very strange and puzzling phenomena) in detail. But they do make it necessary to bear in mind the possibility that important changes in the interaction of the actin units *with each other* may be occurring during the cycles of attachment of the cross bridges.

To conclude then, one might say that the sliding filament model provides a reasonable and promising basis for attempts to describe contraction in detailed molecular terms. It enables one to translate many observable phenomena in muscle into the corresponding events at or near the molecular level, and so to lay down fairly detailed requirements which the molecular mechanism must satisfy. It leads one to hope that more detailed structural knowledge of the arrangements of the actin and myosin molecules in their respective filaments, of the structure of the cross bridges, and of the repetitive changes which must be occurring in some of these during contraction, will bring us nearer to a proper understanding of how this fascinating process takes place.

REFERENCES

Bennett, H. S., and Porter, K. R. (1953). *Am. J. Anat.* **93**, 61.
Corsi, A., and Perry, S. V. (1958). *Biochem. J.* **68**, 12.

Draper, M. H., and Hodge, A. J. (1949). *Australian Exptl. Biol. Med. Sci.* **27**, 465.

Hall, C. E., Jakus, M. A., and Schmitt, F. O. (1946). *Biol. Bull.* **90**, 32.

Hanson, J., and Huxley, H. E. (1953). *Nature* **172**, 530.

Hanson, J., and Huxley, H. E. (1957). *Biochim. et Biophys. Acta* **29**, 250.

Hasselbach, W. (1952). *Z. Naturforsch.* **7b** 164.

Hasselbach, W. (1953). *Z. Naturforsch.* **8b**, 449

Hill, A. V. (1938). *Proc. Roy. Soc.* **B126**, 136.

Hill, A. V. (1949). *Proc. Roy. Soc.* **B136**, 195.

Hodge, A. J., Huxley, H. E., and Spiro, D. (1954). *J. Exptl. Med.* **99**, 208.

Huxley, A. F. (1957). *Progr. in Biophys. and Biophys. Chem.* **7**, 257.

Huxley, A. F., and Niedergerke, R. (1954). *Nature* **176**, 1068.

Huxley, H. E. (1952). Ph.D. Thesis, University of Cambridge, Cambridge.

Huxley, H. E. (1953a). *Proc. Roy. Soc.* **B141**, 59.

Huxley, H. E. (1953b). *Biochim. et Biophys. Acta* **12**, 387.

Huxley, H. E. (1957). *J. Biophys. Biochem. Cytol.* **3**, 631.

Huxley, H. E., and Hanson, J. (1954). *Nature* **173**, 973.

Huxley, H. E., and Hanson, J. (1957). *Biochim. et Biophys. Acta* **23**, 229.

Morgan, C., Rosza, G., Szent-Györgyi, A., and Wyckoff, R. W. G. (1950). *Science* **111**, 201.

Straub, F. B., and Feuer, G. (1950). *Biochim et Biophys. Acta* **4**, 455.

Szent-Györgyi, A. G. (1953). *Arch. Biochem. Biophys.* **42**, 305.

Tsao, T. C. (1953). *Biochim. et Biophys. Acta* **11**, 227, 236.

The Heat Production of Muscle

A. V. HILL

University College London, England

Why is measurement of the heat production of muscle important? Chiefly, because the energy used in contraction is derived from chemical change, and the major part of it appears as heat, the remainder as external mechanical work. One can admit freely that even the most precise description of the energy liberation, in quantity and time course, cannot tell one unequivocally what are the chemical processes involved. But the latter are very difficult to measure directly on living muscle, because of the extremely small quantities involved and because of the slowness of most chemical methods. The measurement of heat is very sensitive and can be made very rapid, so that, although not specific to any particular chemical reaction, it can be made to give evidence of what is going on, and when. In a muscle twitch, the total heat produced is about 3 millicalories per gram. It can be measured to a few parts in a thousand, and localized to within a few milliseconds. If the heat were derived from a chemical process giving, for instance, 10^4 cal/mole, the chemical breakdown would amount to 3×10^{-7} mole per gram. To measure this at all is a pretty difficult task, to locate it within a few milliseconds would require physical methods that are only occasionally applicable. Most chemical methods involve the destruction of the material, so that repeated observations under varied conditions are not possible. The natural method of increasing the quantities to be measured, by using a large number of stimuli in succession, leads to confusion, since then only total quantities are observed, not the time course of the primary event.

When a muscle is excited by a single maximal shock, its heat production begins very early and starts off at practically its maximum rate. The first phase of the heat seems to be a sign, and accompaniment, of chemical reactions by which the muscle

17

is transformed very rapidly from a physicochemical state of rest to a new state of activity, i.e., of readiness to shorten, to develop tension, and to do work. This heat, which is called the "heat of activation," is about 40% of the whole energy ordinarily given out in a twitch; but the fraction is variable, depending on the amount of mechanical work done and the amount of shortening that occurs. By two simple tricks, the heat of activation can be isolated and made to appear as the only external sign of the response to the stimulus. These are: (a) to load the muscle very heavily so that it does not shorten at all and develops no extra tension; and (b) to soak the muscle in a hypertonic solution, of osmotic pressure about three times that of normal Ringer's solution; under these conditions also a muscle shows no visible mechanical response in a twitch. But in both states the muscle produces heat, in amount about equal to that which is ordinarily recognized by other means as heat of activation.

Under normal conditions, the heat of activation starts off, and proceeds to an appreciable extent, before any shortening can be detected or any tension measured. The gap between heat and mechanical response can be lengthened by treatment of a muscle with a moderately hypertonic solution. The immediate effect of a stimulus is to "trigger" some chemical reaction by which the condition of the muscle is temporarily transformed into the contractile state. This new state can be maintained by repeating the stimulus, as in a tetanus; then the heat, which in a twitch is recognized as the heat of activation, becomes the heat associated with the continued maintenance of contraction. This last has been known for many years; it goes on all the time that contraction is maintained, even when no shortening occurs or work is done.

Under normal conditions, when a muscle is activated by a stimulus two things follow, it shortens and it develops a force. When it shortens, it gives out an extra amount of heat proportional to the shortening, and this is the same, per centimeter of shortening, whatever the work it does and whatever the load it has to lift. If we accept the current theory of contraction, when actin and myosin filaments creep along one another there is heat production, and, presumably, chemical breakdown, proportional to the extent of the creep. If the distance shortened be x, the heat is ax, where a has the dimensions of a force; a is found empirically to be about $\frac{1}{4}$ of the maximum force which the muscle can exert when it is not allowed to shorten at all. If the muscle is allowed to shorten, it will do mechanical work against a load. This work is *not* subtracted from the heat of shortening, but appears as a separate and independent item in the energy balance sheet. Again in terms of the current theory, when the actin and myosin filaments creep along one another against an external resistance, doing external work, the chemical breakdown is the sum of two quantities, one proportional to the amount of creep, the other providing energy equal to the work.

In principle, it is possible for a muscle to contract completely isometrically, i.e., at constant length, neither shortening nor doing any mechanical work. Then the total energy liberated would be less by the heat of shortening and the work. In practice, at least with the muscles commonly used, the presence of elastic tendons, by which alone external attachment can be made, requires a muscle to shorten before it can develop external force. Even if tendons were absent altogether, as in some insects' wing muscles, internal shortening might still occur, by one portion of a fiber stretching another portion: this could happen normally in striated fibers by one band of a sarcomere shortening and stretching the other band. It could happen also in any fiber, if one region were stronger than another, and since many fibers are hundreds of times longer than they are thick that does not seem at all unlikely. Nobody, in fact, has ever witnessed a really isometric twitch. If we knew how the tension would rise in such a truly isometric twitch, we could imitate it experimentally on an actual muscle by applying an artificial stretch timed in such a way as to neutralize the internal shortening: then the heat of shortening and the work would be absent. To do this precisely is not possible; nevertheless, by trial and error it is possible, by an appropriate stretch, to get a large reduction in the energy given out by a muscle. The stretch, say, 1/20 of the muscle's length, begins soon after a stimulus and runs its course at some prearranged speed. The work (W) done on the muscle is measured; so is the total heat produced, H_s. H_s contains W, which is degraded into heat when the muscle relaxes, so $H_s - W$ is the net energy given out by the muscle. This is compared with H_i, the energy liberated in an ordinary isometric contraction: $(H_s - W)/H_i$ may be as small as 0.6, showing that the heat of shortening and the work have been largely abolished by the stretch, just as though the muscle had remained genuinely isometric throughout. Thus, although it is physically impossible to obtain a really isometric contraction, it *is* possible, by a small and approximately timed stretch, to prevent shortening and mechanical work and so to reduce the energy given out by the muscle to little more than the heat of activation alone.

The relation between heat produced and tension developed in an isometric twitch allows one to make an approximate calculation of the amount of chemical breakdown involved in developing a force of 1 dyne in a length of 1 cm. This requires an assumption of the total energy per mole in the chemical reaction involved. If we take 6000 cal/mole, we are not likely to be out by more than a factor of 2 either way. This is 2.5×10^{11} ergs/mole. In a muscle twitch conducted as nearly isometrically as possible, the relation is found, $Pl_o/H = 13$ about, where P is force developed in dynes, l_o is standard resting length in centimeters and H is heat produced in ergs. But we have just seen that in any actual "isometric" contraction, there is a substantial amount of mechanical work (which is turned into heat in relaxation) and also of heat of shortening. If the contraction were really isometric, the value of Pl_o/H would be about 20. Thus, in developing a force of 1 dyne in 1 cm length of muscle, the energy used is 0.05 erg. On the assumption of 2.5×10^{11} ergs/mole, 0.05 erg represents a chemical change of 2×10^{-13} mole.

The ultimate unit of a muscle fiber is a sarcomere, and if we take this to be 2.5 μ long, the energy required to develop a force of 1 dyne in a length of 1 sarcomere would be 1.25×10^{-5} erg. This would represent a chemical change of 5×10^{-17} mole, or 3×10^7 molecules. This number is the same whether we consider a fiber, a fibril, or a single unit of actin and myosin filaments. If we wish to calculate the actual number of molecules split, we need to know the force developed.

A similar calculation can be made about the heat of shortening. The heat of shortening x cm is ax, where a is about $P_o/4$: compare this with the energy required to develop a force isometrically in x cm, which is $Px/20$. x can be one sarcomere, or any other distance we like. In any length of muscle, therefore, the energy required to develop maximum force without any shortening is the same as the heat associated with shortening 1/5 of that length. Both these numbers may be useful in calculations. They are independent of temperature.

Another peculiar quantitative relation exists, at least approximately, which also may have a bearing on theories of contraction. Consider the empirical relation between the velocity of shortening (v) and the load (P), $(P + a)$ $(v + b) = $ constant. Here a is a force and b is a velocity, their values can be obtained by making a few records of isotonic shortening, with different loads. It is found empirically that the quantity ab is approximately equal to the rate of liberation of energy during a maintained isometric tetanus. Now b is a velocity, cm/sec., and a is a force: but it has been found that a is the same a as appeared before in the expression, ax, for the heat of shortening a distance x, expressed, of course, in mechanical units. Thus, ab is the rate at which heat of shortening would appear if a muscle were to shorten with velocity b. There is no reason *a priori* that one can see why the chemical and energetic expense of maintaining a contraction at constant length should be the same as the expense of shortening with velocity b. But it is approximately equal—which is a striking fact for they might have been orders of quantities apart. Perhaps, on current theory, the rate at which the bonds between actin and myosin filaments have to be renewed during steady maintained contraction is equal to the frequency with which they move past one another during shortening with velocity b. If so, why? At any rate, here is another useful number to remember.

Hitherto no mention has been made of the heat liberated in muscle when it relaxes. In the simplest case, when a muscle has lifted a load which falls back in relaxation, extra heat is produced equal to the mechanical energy in the load. When a muscle contracts isometrically, elastic energy is developed in its

tendons and other noncontractile parts of it, and this elastic
energy is degraded into heat in relaxation. If, at the height of
an isometric contraction, the elastic energy is taken out of it by
the rapid release of an ergometer to which it is attached, then no
more heat appears. If a muscle is connected to an ergometer
which applies a decreasing load to it as it shortens, a load
which becomes zero at about the stage when normally relaxation begins, then no more heat is found. The absence of heat
production under these conditions does not prove that no chemical reactions are taking place, but only that their net thermal
effect is nil. The fact may be a guide in theories of the chemical
processes, if any, which occur during relaxation.

The elastic state of muscles has been much discussed and
thermal phenomena throw light on this. Resting muscle, in the
region of its normal length, has a rubberlike or thermokinetic
elasticity. A gentle stretch straightens out the molecular chains,
increases their orderliness, and decreases their entropy. Thus,
there is a production of heat during a stretch, an absorption of
heat during a release. This corresponds to the fact, long known,
that a resting muscle shortens on being warmed, lengthens on
being cooled. This is an oversimplified statement of the facts,
but gives a general idea of the condition of a resting muscle.
In fact, the state of affairs is a good deal more complicated than
in rubber, there are several different components, and processes
analogous to crystallization and its reversal appear to occur
when a resting muscle is stretched and released.

The elastic condition of an active muscle is much harder to
investigate. A muscle is maintained in a state of activity only by
continual chemical reaction, and static experiments on its elastic
state are out of the question. Dynamic experiments are needed.
To sudden small stretches an active muscle appears to be
highly inextensible; after a sudden release of quite small extent,
its tension drops to zero. The most significant information is
derived from the thermal effect of a very rapid release applied
when a muscle is at the height of its tension in an isometric contraction (Fig. 1). Immediately on release, and before any appreciable shortening has occurred, there is a rise of temperature,

associated with the loss of tension. The heat ΔQ thus instantaneously produced can be expressed by the equation:

$$\Delta Q = 0.018 \, l_o \, (-\Delta P)$$

where l_o is the standard length and $-\Delta P$ is the fall of tension.

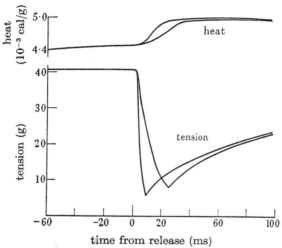

FIG. 1. Copies of records of heat and tension during isometric contractions released 0.65 mm, fast and slow, 0.16 second after the end of a 1-second tetanus. Toad's sartorius at 0° C. (From A. V. Hill, *Proc. Roy. Soc.* **141B**, 168, 1953.)

If the elasticity of active muscle were rubberlike, the constant of the equation would be negative, the muscle would cool when released. The constant 0.018 is considerably greater than for metals, but about the same as for ebonite (hard rubber) and wood. It seems that active muscle has normal and not thermokinetic elasticity. Where this elasticity resides, whether in the A- or the I-bands of the sarcomere, or in both, cannot be stated, and one can see no present way of finding out. But the comparison with ebonite is striking. This is obtained from rubber by heating it with sulfur, and the sulfur links together neighboring long molecular chains, depriving them of their thermokinetic properties and producing a body which has normal and not rubberlike elasticity. The same thing happens in muscle when stimulated. On the current theory of contraction, can we regard the sudden cross-linking of actin and myosin chains resulting from a stimulus as the cause of the elastic transformation, from the rubberlike to the hard rubberlike elastic state?

An interesting confirmation of this result, on the elasticity of active muscle, was obtained by Aubert[*] working on muscles in the peculiar state of rigor induced by stimulation following poisoning with iodoacetate. In such muscles, a release of tension causes a rise of temperature, as it does in normal muscle during the activity caused by stimulation. This is in keeping with the general idea that this state of rigor, which comes on when the whole of the ATP present has been split, has some likeness to the active state temporarily produced by stimulation.

---

[*] Aubert, X., 1956. "Le Couplage Énergétique de la Contraction Musculaire," pp. 272-285. Éditions Arscia, Bruxelles

Chemical Reactions during Contraction and Relaxation*

HANS H. WEBER

Institut für Physiologie im Max-Planck-Institut für medizinische Forschung, Heidelberg, Germany

Since this symposium is chiefly intended for discussion and since the introductory lectures are to serve as a basis for it, I feel that it is not useful to present a complete and detailed picture of the biochemistry of the muscle. Instead, I will confine myself to a sketch in which I shall emphasize the gaps in our present knowledge as a basis for general consideration.

We know from Emden and Parnass and particularly from the eminent biochemist, Meyerhof, and his well-known pupil, Lohmann, that lactic acid fermentation has no other purpose than the formation of adenosine triphosphate (ATP) from adenosine diphosphate (ADP) and inorganic phosphate (P). In addition, we know from a large number of scientists, some of whom are present in this room, that the same is true of the oxidative energy-yielding metabolism.

The experiments of A. V. Hill, especially those carried out during the historically significant period of his collaboration with Meyerhof, have shown us that all the processes leading to the demonstrated ATP formation take place during the anaerobic and aerobic *restitution* phase. Consequently, the energy transformed during the *working* phase can originate only from the *splitting* of the formed or restituted ATP. We ask whether this energy is transferred directly to the contractile structures; for it is conceivable that the energy is transferred from the ATP to another intermediate, and only then to the contractile structure.

In experiments with living muscle, attempts have been made to answer this question by measuring the ATP level during and

---

* In this paper a few paragraphs are reprinted by permission of the publishers from "The Motility of Muscle and Cells," Hans H. Weber, Harvard University Press, Cambridge, Massachusetts. Copyright 1958, by The President and Fellows of Harvard College.

directly after the performance of moderate work at low temperature. It was reasoned that the ATP level would decrease temporarily during the working phase if the energy liberated by ATP splitting were transferred directly to the contractile structure. A significant decrease of the ATP level is never found in the case of performance of moderate work. In general there is only a reduction of the phosphocreatine level, because the restoration of ATP by transphosphorylation from phosphocreatine occurs just as rapidly as the splitting of ATP. Recently Britton Chance (1) with his elegant method corrected this result a little, showing that the ATP level does fall somewhat even with single twitches of the muscle, but so little that the ATP splitting thus evidenced is far from being sufficient to meet the energy requirement of the twitch. In very recent and systematic work carried out by Krebs, Fleckenstein, Davies and co-workers (2) on the one hand, and by Mommaerts (3) on the other, it has been shown in addition that in the case of the performance of very little work at near 0° C not even the phosphocreatine level is measurably reduced.

All these observations seem to indicate that the energy liberated by ATP splitting is *not* transferred *directly* to the contractile system. Principally, however, it may be objected to this interpretation that the ATP splitting during the working phase can be much greater than the reduction of the ATP level, because the ATP level may be the result of both processes—ATP splitting and ATP resynthesis occurring at the same time (i.e., the change in the ATP turnover can be much greater than in the ATP level). The experiments of Krebs, Fleckenstein, and co-workers (2), as well as those of Mommaerts (3), approach this problem from an entirely different premise than those of Britton Chance (1). Therefore I do not want to anticipate the discussion of this point in my lecture.

The situation becomes much simpler when the analysis of the working phase is carried out with isolated contractile systems rather than with living muscle; for with the isolation of the contractile systems, the multiplicity of the ATP restoring processes is excluded. Isolated contractile systems are capable of splitting ATP, and thus of contracting with performance of work (4–6). On the other hand, they are not capable of restoring the split ATP.

The washed muscle fibrils which Dr. H. E. Huxley has just described are examples of such isolated systems taken from cross-striated muscles. They have been introduced into scientific research in Chicago (7), and especially in Cambridge, England, by Perry (8). It is possible to leave the fibrils and contractile elements of movable cells in the tissue. If the cell and muscle membranes are destroyed and all soluble proteins, enzymes, and substrates of metabolism are extracted, the entire muscle fiber (4–6) and cell (9) behave as if they were composed only of the isolated contractile structures. This method was developed for muscle fibers by Albert Szent-Györgyi (4) and for cells by Hoffmann-Berling (9).

Finally the contractile protein can be extracted from muscle and cells and purified by the usual methods of protein chemistry (10, 11). From the solution of these highly purified proteins, well-oriented threads can then be produced, which likewise contract with the performance of work upon the addition of appropriate chemical substances (10, 11). This so-called acto-myosin thread was produced for the first time in my laboratory 25 years ago (12).

In a physiological ionic environment all these isolated contractile systems split added ATP and thereby contract. If the ATP splitting is reversibly inhibited by poisons (13) or by a physiological factor (14, 15) originating from the muscle granules (16), then a reversible relaxation occurs.

We know from countless experiments during the last 10 years that the contraction of isolated contractile structures is more or less the same as the contraction of living muscles and cells (5). Maximal tension and its dependence on temperature, maximal shortening, speed of shortening, and efficiency are quantitatively the same (5, 6). The identity extends so far, that the differences existing among the various muscle and cell types with respect to these phenomena can also be found in the isolated contractile systems prepared from these different muscles and cells (17).

Thus, it is well established that the isolated contractile systems of all types of muscles as well as of many movable cells require

ATP as an operative substance for the contraction cycle. In its function as an operative substance, ATP can be replaced by any one of the nucleoside triphosphates (NTP) so far investigated (18). The mechanical power of the contractile systems is greatest, however, with ATP. A particularly significant reduction in mechanical power is observed when the six —NH_2 nucleoside triphosphates are replaced by six —OH nucleoside triphosphates (18). None of the other known substances participating in ATP restitution has any effect. It makes no difference whether or not these other substances contain energy-rich phosphate bonds. Thus, we see that the reaction between ATP and the contractile structure is quite a specific one. This is a strong argument in favor of the physiological significance of ATP.

The conclusion that ATP splitting is a prerequisite for contraction, and that its inhibition results in relaxation and renders contraction impossible, still does not account completely for the interaction between ATP and contractile structure; for, if the ATP splitting in an isolated contractile system is interrupted not by inhibition but by the removal of ATP, the system does not relax but becomes rigid (13). The presence of ATP, i.e., the binding of ATP to the contractile structure, without simultaneous ATP splitting, has a plasticizing effect (13), and in its function as a plasticizer, ATP can be replaced not only by other nucleoside triphosphates, but also by any other inorganic polyphosphate (13).

From the results reported so far, it may be concluded that ATP functions as a contracting substance in all muscles and in many cells providing that it is split by the contractile structures. If it is merely bound by these structures, however, and not split, then its effect is that of a relaxing or plasticizing substance. ATP splitting, however, by any ATPase other than the contractile protein system does not result in contraction.

Since living muscle always contains ATP, the above conclusion means that the relaxation phase of muscle contraction is not an active process, but simply the end of the ATP splitting and of the contraction phase of the contraction cycle thus induced. This interpretation is in perfect agreement with the mechanical and thermodynamic results obtained by A. V. Hill in experiments with *living* muscle.

We have heard from H. E. Huxley that the contraction of the muscle fibril is not caused by a *shortening* of the fine filaments within the fibril, but by a *sliding* of the actin filaments alongside the L-myosin filaments. This brings us to the question of conceiving a mechanism through which ATP splitting can result in a sliding of actin filaments alongside L-myosin filaments. In order to find such a mechanism, we have only to modify, in one single point, the well-known metabolic reactions in which the energy liberated by ATP splitting is required for chemical synthesis.

Let us select as a model of such a metabolic reaction the synthesis of fatty acid chains from acetate by coenzyme A in the presence of ATP and Mg.

(1). acetate$^-$ + A—P $\sim$ P $\sim$ P $\rightleftharpoons$ A—P $\sim$ acetate + P $\sim$ P
Activation of the COOH group of the acetate.

(2). A—P $\sim$ acetate + HS—CoA $\rightleftharpoons$ acetate $\sim$ SCoA + AMP
First reaction of the activated COOH group with the SH group of coenzyme A.

(3). acetate $\sim$ SCoA + acetate $\sim$ SCoA
$\rightleftharpoons$ acetoacetyl $\sim$ SCoA + HSCoA
Second reaction of the activated COOH group with the CH$_3$ group of another CoA—S acetate.

(4). Further reaction of similar type forming longer carbon chains.

Such a series of reactions leads to a sliding of filaments if we make the following additional assumptions: (1) The group activated by transphosphorylation is attached to the one filament. (2) The various functional groups reacting successively with this active group are arranged in a linear periodicity alongside the other filament.

"A sequence of reactions during the course of which the active group of one filament successively reacts with several linearly arranged groups of the other filament has the inevitable result that the active group travels alongside the other filament while being shifted from the first to the last of the groups involved" (from H. H. Weber, see footnote, page 25) (Fig. 1).

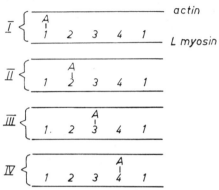

FIG. 1. Shifting of one filament alongside another filament produced by a sequence of chemical reactions. A = active group of the actin filament. 1, 2, 3, 4 = groups of the L-myosin filament successively reacting with A.

Consequently we suppose that the terminal phosphate residue of the ATP is transferred, for example, to an acid group of the actin filament activating this group (Fig. 2); that is, the activation of the acid group. We assume that this phosphate residue is exchanged with a sulfhydryl group of the L-myosin filament. This corresponds to the conversion of acetyl-adenosine-5'-phosphate (AC-AMP) into acetyl-coenzyme A, the second step of fatty acid synthesis.

In neither of these reactions is there a liberation of energy; for the free energy of the terminal phosphate bond in the ATP, like the binding of phosphate to an acid group of the actin filament, and like the sulfhydryl-ester bond between actin and L-myosin filament has a standard energy of about 8000 cal. However, the succeeding reactions of the activated group of the actin filament with further functional groups of the L-myosin filament must liberate energy; for the shift of the actin filament alongside the L-myosin filament during contraction implies performance of work. The energy contained in the sulfhydryl-ester bond is almost completely liberated if at the conclusion of the sequence of reactions the filaments are united by means of a normal ester bond. For such an ester bond contains only about 2000–3000 cal. There may be one or two bonds containing a medium amount of energy between the first and the last types of bonds.

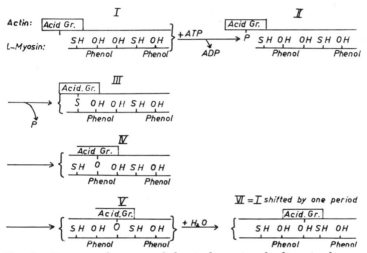

FIG. 2. Diagram of a series of chemical reactions leading simultaneously to ATP hydrolysis and to a shifting of the molecules of the actin filaments alongside the molecules of L-myosin filaments. The figures I to VI denote successive chemical conditions and stages of shifting.

Consequently it is supposed that the active group of actin is passed along from the bond of the SH group by the bond of a phenolic OH group to a bond of an alcoholic OH group. Subsequently this normal ester bond is hydrolyzed, and the acid group of actin is rephosphorylated. Afterward the sequence of reactions represented begins anew.

"Since the rephosphorylated actin group is now close to the sulfhydryl group of the next period and remote from the sulfhydryl group of the first period, the active actin group is shifted alongside the *next* longitudinal period of the L-myosin filament if the muscle is unloaded. The single shifting steps without interruption amount to the visible external shortening which can be measured.

"The more heavily the muscle is loaded, however, the more frequently during rephosphorylation the actin filament with its active group is withdrawn by the load into the initial position. This increases the number of shifting steps necessary for the fibril to shorten by a definite amount. As a result, the amount of energy released per centimeter of shortening increases the more heavily the muscle is loaded" (from H. H. Weber, see footnote, page 25).

On the other hand, the loading of the muscle counteracting the shortening can be interpreted as an apparent increase of the activation energy of reactions III to V of Fig. 2 which induce the shortening. Therefore, the more heavily the muscle is loaded the more slowly these reaction steps succeed one another. This means, however, that the liberation of energy decreases with increasing load if it is calculated in terms of unit of time, and not in terms of centimeters of shortening. Both consequences of the suggested reaction scheme—increasing liberation of energy per centimeter of shortening, decreasing liberation per unit of time with increasing load—have been established in the classic work of A. V. Hill on the thermodynamics of the *living* muscle.

This principle of the proposed sequence of chemical reactions may require modifications in detail. I should like to present several arguments in favor of this principle for our discussion of this reaction scheme:

(1). In contrast to the earlier theories of contraction the proposed reaction sequence leads to thermodynamic results, at least qualitatively, that agree with the above-mentioned thermodynamic observations made by A. V. Hill on living muscle.

(2). It is certain that not only the contraction of the actomyosin system but also the Mg-activated ATP *splitting* is due to an interaction between actin and L-myosin; for under physiological conditions, the rate of Mg-activated ATP splitting by actomyosin is about ten times as great as the splitting rate of the components actin and L-myosin when separated. On the other hand, Hasselbach (19) has shown that ATP splitting in the living muscle is activated by Mg.

(3). It is quite likely that the transfer of energy from ATP to the working system takes place by means of transphosphorylation. This is true of all the cases investigated so far in which the energy of ATP splitting is required for chemical processes. There are a number of experimental indications that the ATP splitting by the contractile structures also begins with transphosphorylation (20, 21).

(4). We have known for a long time that the contraction of the isolated contractile systems and the ATP splitting by these systems are completely inhibited, if the SH groups of the actomyosin are blocked or destroyed (5).

(5). Some recent unpublished observations concerning the mechanism of the physiological *relaxation* phase can be explained easily by the principle suggested. This will be illustrated in greater detail.

It is understandable that in the presence of ATP relaxation always occurs when ATP splitting is inhibited. But relaxation is also induced by means of the *physiological relaxing factor,* although this factor does not inhibit ATP splitting completely even in the highest concentrations (Fig. 3). This relaxing factor was discovered by Marsh and Bendall and shown by Portzehl to be a product of certain muscle granules. This factor brings about total relaxation if the Mg-activated ATP splitting is reduced by the relaxing factor to approximately 10% of the normal ATP splitting (Fig. 3). The speed of this residual splitting, however, which cannot be suppressed by the factor is *exactly the same* as the speed of the ATP splitting occurring in the actomyosin system when the actin and the L-myosin are completely dissociated from each other.

That the factor dissociates actin and L-myosin in the presence of ATP can also be shown in another way. We know from H. E. Huxley that the slipping of the actin filaments from the L-myosin filaments is responsible for the fact that muscle fibrils can be easily stretched under ATP. Therefore, the degree of association of both types of filaments can also be determined from the resistance against stretch. Table I shows that this resistance, that is to say, the association of actin and L-myosin filaments, is greatest in the rigid state (in rigor) when no plasticizing polyphosphates are present. Furthermore, this table shows that the association of the filaments is still great when ATP is present and is split at the same time, that is, during contraction. This is understandable from the reaction scheme which was described.

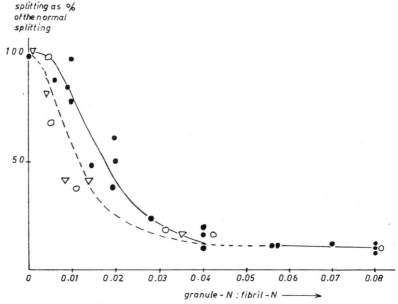

FIG. 3. Dependence of ATP splitting on the proportion of granules to fibrils. KEY: •, 0.4 mg protein/cc; o, 4 mg protein/cc; inverted triangle, 9 mg protein/cc.

During relaxation the resistance to stretch is by far the smallest, since the interaction between actin and L-myosin, which depends upon ATP splitting, is absent. There is, however, a very considerable difference between the relaxation produced by mersalyl and the relaxation brought about by the factor. In the case of factor-induced relaxation the static resistance is zero (Table I). Both the kinetics of the ATP splitting and the complete disappearance of the resistance to stretch under the influence of the relaxing factor indicate that the factor has no relaxing effect, because it inhibits ATP splitting incompletely. On the contrary, the difference between ATPase poisons and the factor

TABLE I

STATIC RESISTANCE AGAINST STRETCH (EXTRACTED MUSCLE FIBERS)

	As $g \times cm^{-2} \times L \times \Delta L^{-1}$
Rigor	~ 10,000
Contraction	~ 5000
Relaxation	
Produced by mersalyl	~ 250[a]
Produced by factor	~ 0[b]

[a] Portzehl (13).
[b] Hasselbach and Weber (22).

strongly suggests that the factor renders contraction impossible and diminishes splitting by preventing any interaction between actin and L-myosin filaments. For this interaction is the prerequisite not only for contraction but also for Mg-activated ATP splitting at a normal rate.

REFERENCES

1. Chance, B., and Connelly, C. M. *Nature* **179**, 1235 (1957).
2. Fleckenstein, A., Janke, J., Davies, R. E., and Krebs, H. A. *Nature* **174**, 1081 (1954).
3. Mommaerts, W. F. H. M. *Am. J. Physiol.* **182**, 585 (1955).
4. Szent-Györgyi, A. *Biol. Bull.* **96**, 140 (1949).
5. Weber, H. H., and Portzehl, H. *Progr. in Biophys. and Biophys. Chem.* **4**, 60 (1954).
6. Ulbrecht, G., and Ulbrecht, M. *Biochim. et Biophys. Acta* **11**, 138 (1953); **13**, 319 (1954).
7. Schick, A. S., and Hass, G. M. *Science* **109**, 487 (1949).
8. Perry, S. V. *Biochem. J.* **48**, 257 (1951).
9. Hoffmann-Berling, H. *Fortschr. Zool.* **11**, 142 (1958).
10. Portzehl, H. *Z. Naturforsch.* **6b**, 355 (1951)
11. Dörr, D., and Portzehl, H. *Z. Naturforsch.* **9b**, 550 (1954).
12. Weber, H. H. *Arch. ges. Physiol., Pflüger's* **235**, 206 (1934).
13. Portzehl, H. *Z. Naturforsch.* **7b**, 1 (1952).
14. Marsh, B. B. *Biochim. et Biophys. Acta* **9**, 247 (1952).
15. Bendall, J. R. *Nature* **170**, 1058 (1952).
16. Portzehl, H. *Biochim. et Biophys. Acta* **26**, 373 (1957); Weber, H. H. *Ann. Rev. Biochem.* **26**, 667 (1957).
17. Weber, H. H. "The Motility of Muscle and Cells," 69 pp. Harvard Univ. Press, Cambridge, Massachusetts, 1958.
18. Hasselbach, W. *Biochim. et Biophys. Acta* **20**, 355 (1956).
19. Hasselbach, W. *Biochim. et Biophys. Acta* **25**, 562 (1957).

20. Ulbrecht, G., and Ulbrecht, M. *Biochim. et Biophys. Acta* **25**, 100 (1957).

21. Ulbrecht, G., Ulbrecht, M., and Wustrow, H. J. *Biochim. et Biophys. Acta* **25**, 110 (1957).

22. Hasselbach, W., and Weber, H. H. *Biochim. et Biophys. Acta* **11**, 160 (1953).

Attempts toward a Formulation of Biological Use of Energy in Terms of Chemical Potentials

FRITZ LIPMANN

The Rockefeller Institute, New York, New York

Chemical and biological definitions are becoming more and more confluent. In this situation, terminologies occasionally need a mutual adjustment for which some common sense has to be used. Cellular chemistry is part of a technology of a very special kind and this aspect often deviates from interests of pure chemistry. Thus, the term "energy-rich" bond and the $\sim$ sign (1) in the biological sense describe energy units in cellular metabolism. Their acceptance and wide use by biologically minded chemists shows the need for this type of description in the context of cellular chemistry.

In expanding and, at the same time, circumscribing the definition of the energy carried in the energy-rich bond, the term group potential was introduced simultaneously (1) because the use of a potential scale appeared to be rather suitable for describing certain phases of energy metabolism.[1] I have often felt that our understanding of the structure of the energy turnover in cellular metabolism would have been eased if an electrode had been available that would measure group potentials, such as the phosphoryl potential in adenosine triphosphate (ATP) or the acetyl potential of co-

---

[1] I prefer the term I originally proposed, i.e., group potential, to group *transfer* potential recently suggested by Klotz (2). Originally, I had recommended measuring group potential as the energy available in a link or expended in forming a link. This would be numerically equal but opposite in sign to the change of free energy with hydrolytic cleavage. I have now changed my mind in this respect and prefer to follow the convention and equate group potential with the change in free energy liberated by cleaving. A negative value for ΔF has, I feel, acquired an essentially positive connotation. Therefore, I do not hesitate to talk about *higher* and *lower* group potentials which, paradoxically, mean more negative or less negative.

enzyme A, (CoA), in a manner similar to the measuring of oxidation-reduction (O/R) potential. In the coupling mechanism between respiration and phosphorylation we actually have an interconversion of O/R potential and phosphoryl potential and, in focusing on the conversion mechanisms, it is often more convenient to use the voltage scale for phosphoryl potential (3). It is useful to remember that in considering a two-electron system,[2] 10 kcal of phosphoryl potential equal approximately 0.2 volts.

The interconvertibility of group potential and electron potential seems to have implications with the theory of coupling reactions. It has already been intimated by Krebs and Kornberg (6) that such interconvertibility should put limitations on the localization of a conversion from O/R to group potential at various levels of the O/R scale. Once converted to group potential, the energy escapes the scaling effect of the oxidation-reduction ladder and this should result in what I like to call a scrambling up of the different oxidation-reduction levels with regard to convertibility. This should account for the rather

---

[2] By interconversion of hydrogen and group potential, the incoming group displaces the hydrogen in the substrate. Taking as an example a reaction (4) such as:

$$\text{acetaldehyde} + \text{CoASH} + \text{DPN}^+ \rightarrow \text{acetyl SCoA} + \text{DPNH}$$

this appears clearly when formulated as follows:

$$
\begin{array}{cc}
\text{O} & \text{O} \\
\uparrow & \uparrow \\
\text{CoA·S:} \rightarrow \text{C:H} \rightarrow \text{DPN}^+ \rightleftharpoons \text{CoA·S·C} & + \text{HDPN} \\
| & | \\
\text{CH}_3 & \text{CH}_3
\end{array}
$$

It appears, then, that the incoming group which confers the group potential on the acyl, ejects a hydride ion, hydrogen being transferred to diphosphopyridine nucleotide (DPN) as a unit, as we know from Vennesland and Westheimer's work (5). I think this formulation shows that in a coupling mechanism an acylium derives from a "dissociation":

$$
\begin{array}{cc}
\text{O} & \text{O} \\
\uparrow & \uparrow \\
\text{RCH} \rightleftharpoons \text{RC}^+ & \ldots : \text{H}^-
\end{array}
$$

and explains the derivation of acetyl, or phosphoryl, or other group potentials from a two-electron transfer.

general experience that, in most cases, uncoupling agents are all-or-nothing reagents and, at saturating concentrations, wipe out the coupling over the whole ladder. This needs a somewhat more thorough work-over, but it shows the advantage of extending the potential scale over the whole energy field of cellular metabolism.

I have considered proposing the use of the voltage scale for the group potential altogether,[3] and I still think that in the minds of biologists, the role of the group potential as the dominant energy potential in all phases of cell metabolism might be more easily understood if such a scale were used. However, since it is a fictional scale having no experimental equivalent, it appears wiser to remain with the caloric scale. But understanding of cellular energy would be helped, I think, if more attention were paid to the fact that the cellular energy potential is often a group potential which, on its way toward use, is generally derived from phosphoryl potential.

SOME CHARACTERISTICS OF THE PHOSPHORYL POTENTIAL IN ATP

One prominent reason why the unavailability of responding electrodes is so regrettable is the present difficulty of measuring a group potential. By definition, a group potential is a measure of the degree of activation of a group in a certain binding, comparing it to what we might call the ground state or the free compound—in our particular case, inorganic phosphate (P). A measure of the activation of the group can be derived from its conversion to the ground state—in our case, the conversion of phosphate terminally bound in ATP to inorganic phosphate through hydrolysis. The higher the group potential, of course, the more energy is liberated in the process of hydrolysis, or is required in reverse for dehydration. Almost the only available values for group potentials are obtained from measurement of the equilibrium between hydrolysis and dehydration, the hydrol-

[3] A number of points raised here have been brought out in Dixon's fine little book on *Multi-Enzyme Systems* (7). Not too much attention has been paid to his discussion partly due, I feel, to the proposition made therein of a relatively unhandy scale for phosphoryl which is borrowed from the rH scale once tried but later abandoned by Mansfield Clark.

ysis constant, and the standard free energy is derived from the hydrolysis constant by:

$$\Delta F^\circ = -RT \times \ln K; \quad K = \frac{ADP \times P}{ATP} \tag{1}$$

To obtain the ΔF value under nonstandard conditions (2), the following derivation should cover the most important aspects of the situation. It introduces a simplified pH-dependence function and is calculated for 30°:

$$\Delta F = \Delta F^\circ - 1400 \log \frac{[ATP]}{[ADP]} + $$
$$1400 \log [P] - 1400 \log \left(1 + \frac{K^*}{[H^+]}\right) \tag{2}$$

I find it quite significant and, as far as I can see, rather unappreciated that the amount of energy derivable from the system depends importantly on the ATP/ADP ratio, the phospho-dephospho quotient, which is analogous to the dependence of O/R potential on O/R ratio, or of hydrogen ion potential on the buffer quotient. The curve drawn in Fig. 1 shows the typical sigmoid character, with the standard potential at mid-point relating to equal amounts of phospho- and dephospho-compound. This curve may be considered a potentiometric titration of adenosine diphosphate (ADP) with a phosphoryl donor of a phosphoryl potential sufficiently higher than that of the ATP/ADP as not to overlap. Such a titration, if there were a phosphoryl electrode, would give us at mid-point the standard potential of the ATP/ADP system. It is quite obvious that what is said here about the phosphoryl system is applicable to an acetyl system, or to any analogous system.

The difference between ratios of ATP to ADP of 1:100 and 100:1, as may be seen in Fig. 1, amounts to as much as 5.4 kcal. In a normal cell at steady state, a fair balancing of phosphate-bond generation by its utilization is expressed by a fairly constant ratio of ATP to ADP not far from unity (8); in other words, the phosphoryl potential is kept nicely buffered. On the other hand, in many systems we need an even supply of phosphoryl to drive a synthetic reaction, and it has been a common experience in studies of biosynthetic reactions that catalytic amounts of ATP, coupled with a large supply of a phosphoryl donor of high potential, work far better than ATP itself. A reason for this is that the ATP/ADP quotient and therefore the phosphoryl potential is evenly kept at high level by the feeder

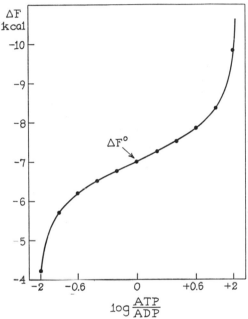

Fig. 1.   Dependence of free energy of ATP hydrolysis on pH, for pK_2 of inorganic phosphate 6.8, using the last term in equation 2 for the calculation.

system. The gradient toward utilization is therefore considerably steeper than it can be if ATP is used and progressively converts to ADP, which makes the phosphoryl potential slide constantly downward.

Since standard potential refers to molar phosphate, it will, at any lower concentrations, require more energy to activate phosphoryl, with an extra expenditure of —1.4 kcal (30°) per logarithmic concentration unit. Intracellular phosphate concentrations appear to be of the order of 10^{-2} to 10^{-3} moles per liter, adding approximately 2.8–4.2 kcal to $\Delta F°$ of ATP. The phosphate concentration effect on the phosphoryl potential must be prominent in oxidative phosphorylation and glycolysis in which P is a component of the system. It cancels out, however, with phosphate shifts between two phosphoryl derivatives.

The pH dependence of $\Delta F°$ for ATP hydrolysis has been exhaustively discussed by Alberty *et al.* (9). A simpler function may be obtained as follows. When ATP is hydrolyzed the terminal pK_2 6.5 of ATP changes to pK_2 6.8 of inorganic phosphate. Two acid functions appear, corresponding to the terminal pK_2 6.3 of ADP and pK_3 11.8 of inorganic phosphate; the latter can be neglected physiologically. This all very closely averages to an appearance of an acid function pK^* of 6.5, and is introduced in the last term in equation 2. Figure 2 shows pH dependence as calculated therefrom.

At pH 7.5, and with a phosphate concentration of 10^{-2}, the average ΔF for phosphoryl potential will be approximately —11 kcal, about —4 kcal greater than the standard potential of the ATP/ADP system which, according to recent evaluation, is probably around —7 kcal (10).

LOCALIZATION OF THE GROUP POTENTIAL

Biological energy transfer has been most successfully developed on examples of group activation with the phosphoryl potential of ATP as the energy donor. Almost every day we learn to appreciate the great versatility of this energy donor because of the obvious ease with which the enzyme apparatus of the cell is able to convert phosphoryl into other group potentials and thus to transact group activation. One will most easily recognize the essential features of this activation process when considering, as an example, the rather frequent activation of a carboxylate ion. The energy transfer by way of the energy-rich phosphate involves the conversion of the $P \cdot O \cdot P$ in a diphosphoanhydride, into a $C \cdot O \cdot P$ in a mixed carboxyl-phosphoanhydride. Therewith, the high phosphoryl potential of ATP converts to a similarly high phosphoryl potential of a phosphoryl acylate. The energy transfer, however, becomes useful really, first through a relocation of the energy due to a "conversion" of a phosphoryl into an acyl potential.

Using the wriggle sign for preliminary localization of the energy, the reaction of the first enzymatic step leading to carboxyl activation is characterized by the enzymatic energy

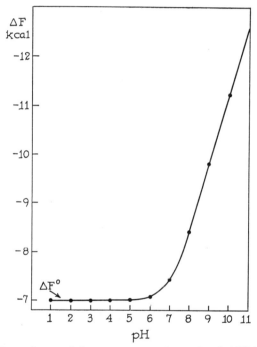

Fig. 2. Dependence of free energy on the ratio of ATP/ADP, assuming a $\Delta F°$ of 7 kcal. The middle term in equation 2 was used for calculation. In the straight derivation of 2 from 1, this term would appear as $+1400 \log$ (ADP/ATP). The inverted $-1400 \log$ (ATP/ADP) is used because it better illustrates the concept of the phosphoryl potential.

transfer from PO $\sim$ P to CO $\sim$ P. To make this transfer useful, however, the mixed anhydride has to react as an active acyl, or the CO $\sim$ P has to become a C $\sim$ OP. Such a shift of emphasis is imposed on the molecule by a change from the transphosphorylation catalyst to the transacylation catalyst. These may be two different enzymes, or different sites on one enzyme protein. To amplify, I will take the clearly defined process of microbial acetate activation where transphosphorylation is separated from transacylation, each being transacted as a separate enzyme. The first step is catalyzed by a kinase transferring the terminal phosphoryl of ATP (*11, 12*). The kinase facilitates the reversible reaction:

$$\text{acetate} + \text{phosphoryl} \sim \text{ADP} \leftrightarrows \text{phosphoryl} \sim \text{acetate} + \text{ADP} \qquad (3)$$

The kinase reaction yields, as yet, only a potentially active acetate. The now terminal phosphate in ADP, the previous neighbor of the phosphoryl, loses access to the energy and, through the newly created CO $\sim$ P situation, acetate becomes the new neighbor and the prospective, but in the transphosphorylase system, not yet actual acceptor of potential. When the transacetylation catalyst (*13*) takes over, catalyzing the reaction:

$$\text{acetyl} \sim \text{phosphate} + \text{CoASH} \leftrightarrows \text{acetyl} \sim \text{SCoA} + \text{phosphate} \qquad (4)$$

the acetyl potential becomes negotiable. The transacetylase realizes the acetyl potential by focusing on the C $\sim$ OP configuration and promoting the acetyl transfer between acetyl phosphate and reduced coenzyme A (CoASH). By this second step, the energy transfer is consummated and the conversion of phosphoryl into acyl potential is completed.

To summarize the situation, the group that is to be brought to reaction in a sequence of activation and transfer, obviously changes character from passive to active, or from substrate to reagent. In our example, in the first step acetate is the substrate and energy acceptor and the phosphoryl of ATP is the reagent and energy donor. In the second step, the phosphoryl acetate of the first step now becomes the reagent, acetyl phosphate. The over-all effect is the conversion of acetate to reactive acetate.

So far, we have dealt with a biological energy transfer in a descriptive manner, using the noncommittal $\sim$ sign for preliminary energy localization. A pointer toward a more precise definition of the chemical meaning of this type of group activation seems to be offered, as discussed by Ingold (*14*), by an apparently rather common reaction that occurs when acetic or similar anhydrides are dissolved in an anhydrous solvent with sulfuric acid. Conductometric measurements show that the anhydride, when dissolved with sulfuric acid, forms completely ionized acylium monosulfate (15) and organic acid:

$$RCOCR + H_2SO_4 \rightarrow RC^+ + HSO_4^- + RCOH \tag{5}$$

This solution, containing the free acylium ion, is a most potent acylation reagent. This invites formulation of an acid anhydride as acylium acylate:

$$RC^+ \ldots {}^-OCR \tag{6}$$

Accordingly, we propose to formulate acetate activation as a conversion of acetate into acetylium, by reaction of acetate with the terminal phosphorylium of ATP:

$$CH_3CO^- + P^+ \ldots {}^-O\,P\,O\,P\,O \cdot adenosine \rightleftarrows$$

$$CH_3CO^- \ldots {}^+P\,O^- + {}^-O\,P\,O\,P\,O \cdot adenosine \tag{7}$$

The mixed anhydride now oscillates around the center oxygen:

$$CH_3CO^- \ldots {}^+P\,O^- \rightleftarrows CH_3C^+ \ldots {}^-O\,P\,O^- \tag{8}$$

The molecule is apparently stabilized by a transphosphorylation enzyme in left-hand form as phosphorylium donor, but by the transacylation step in the right-hand form as an acylium donor.

The definitions of active acetate, or more generally active acylate, as an acylium, active phosphate as phosphorylium, and active sulfate as sulfurylium, are very attractive and give a more tangible description to the group potential as a partial, positive charge or latent ionization tendency. The function of the enzymes that catalyze the two reactions in the activation and transfer steps would then be to catalyze a phosphorylium exchange in the activation and an acylium shift in the utilization step.

We propose that, very generally speaking, the essential feature of the activation by phosphorylium transfer is the creation of a potential acylium. By defining the positively charged acylium or phosphorylium as the reactants, the type of reaction becomes electrophilic, rather than nucleophilic as has frequently been proposed. It is necessary, in any case, to formulate the reaction in the manner of a push-pull reaction, since enzymatic catalysts are always involved which exert strong, directing forces or, more explicitly, electron-pulling influences on the donor molecule.

CONCLUSION

The definition of ATP as a phosphorylium donor could lead to a better understanding of such sequences of energy transfer where we are pretty much in the dark about events subsequent to an initial ATP-involving step. Such is sadly needed for the conversion of phosphoryl potential into osmotic as well as into mechanical work. However, some hope appeared recently for developing a formulation of muscle contraction, favored by those primed by familiarity with biosynthetic mechanisms, namely, a transfer of the phosphorylium to the contracting protein (16). The recent work by Levy and Koshland (17) on O^{18} exchange of phosphoryl with water that appears to take place immediately after reaction of ATP with myosin, is the first experimental encouragement for such a formulation. The situation, however, is not simple since many attempts to show phosphoryl exchange between contractile protein and ATP have been discouraging.

In the case of osmotic work, the connection with a phosphorylium transfer mechanism is worse, and is merely suggested by the disruption of concentration effects by uncoupling reagents such as dinitrophenol. Any easy chemical interpretation of a coupling of osmotic work with the energy derived from the phosphoryl potential of ATP has so far been rather disappointing and a new departure needs to be found. But still, although a continuity of energy transmission is lacking, the initial energy release appears almost certainly to take off from the phosphoryl of ATP, and whatever we can do to understand this energy better should eventually smooth our way toward the approach to these, at present, seemingly thorny problems.

REFERENCES

1. Lipmann, F. *Advances in Enzymol.* **1**, 99 (1941).
2. Klotz, I. M. "Some Principles of Energetics in Biochemical Reactions." Academic Press, New York, 1957.
3. Lipmann, F. *In* "Currents of Biochemical Research" (D. E. Green, ed.), p. 137. Interscience, New York, 1946.
4. Burton, R. M., and Stadtman, E. R. *J. Biol. Chem.* **202**, 873 (1953).
5. Vennesland, B., and Westheimer, F. H. *In* "The Mechanism of Enzyme Action," p. 357. Johns Hopkins Press, Baltimore, Maryland, 1954.
6. Krebs, H. A., and Kornberg, H. L. "Energy Transformations in Living Matter." Springer, Berlin, 1957.
7. Dixon, M. "Multi-Enzyme Systems." Cambridge Univ. Press, London and New York, 1949.
8. Lynen, F., Hartmann, G., Netter, K. F., and Schuegraf, A. *Ciba Foundation Symposium, Regulation Cell Metabolism*, p. 256 (1959).
9. Alberty, R. A., Smith, R. M., and Bloch, R. M. *J. Biol. Chem.* **193**, 425 (1951).
10. Morales, M. F., Botts, J., Blum, J. J., and Hill, T. L. *Physiol. Revs.* **35**, 475 (1955).
11. Lipmann, F. *Advances in Enzymol.* **6**, 231 (1946).
12. Rose, I. A. *In* "Methods in Enzymology" (S. P. Colowick and N. O. Kaplan, eds.), Vol. 1, p. 591. Academic Press, New York, 1955.
13. Stadtman, E. R., Novelli, G. D., and Lipmann, F. *J. Biol. Chem.* **191**, 365 (1951).
14. Ingold, C. K. "Structure and Mechanism in Organic Chemistry," p. 296. Cornell Univ. Press, Ithaca, New York, 1953.
15. Gillespie, R. J. *J. Chem. Soc.* p. 2997 (1950).
16. Weber, H. H. "The Motility of Muscle and Cells." Harvard Univ. Press, Cambridge, Massachusetts, 1958.
17. Levy, H. M., Koshland, D. E., Jr. *J. Biol. Chem.* **234**, 1102 (1959).

Some Considerations of Structure and Function in Proteins

BARBARA W. LOW

*Department of Biochemistry, College of Physicians and Surgeons,
Columbia University, New York*

I have been asked to comment on the relationship between structure and function in proteins—particularly in globular proteins. We do not now know the complete three-dimensional molecular structure of any protein molecule. Nor can we describe protein function critically in terms of well-defined chemical reactions or physicochemical properties. We cannot, therefore, discuss possible relationships between structure and function with exactitude or authority; such discussions must be speculative, and the arguments teleological. We all accept the view that biological function is explicable in terms of molecular structure, not simply as a truism, but specifically in terms of the three-dimensional molecular architecture of the native protein molecule. Further, we expect there to be simple unifying principles of structural design.

Happily, there are now some analytical descriptions of the probable configurations of proteins which are not speculative. We may first establish these features in terms of the α-helix structure of Pauling *et al.* (1951). The peptide chains of proteins may be represented

$$\begin{array}{ccccc} R_1 & R_2 & R_3 & R_4 & R_n \\ | & | & | & | & | \end{array}$$
$$NH_2CHCO\cdot NHCHCO\cdot NHCHCO\cdot NHCHCO \ldots NHCHCOOH$$

Whatever the sequence of the amino acid residues R_1, R_2, R_3 . . . R_n, the peptide backbone chain has a simple repeating unit —NH·CH·CO— .

From the detailed crystal structure studies of amino acids and some simple peptides, precise dimensions for this peptide chain residue (NH·CH·CO) were derived (Fig. 1). The amide group is planar; there is almost 50% double bond character in the C—N bond which is consequently shorter (1.32 A) than the normal single C—N bond length of 1.47 A. The drawing shows the *trans* configuration of the amide group which appears more stable than the alternative *cis*

$$
\begin{array}{ccc}
\text{C} & & \text{C} \\
\diagdown & & \diagup \\
& \text{C} - \text{N} & \\
\diagup\diagup & & \diagdown \\
\text{O} & & \text{H}
\end{array}
$$

configuration (Pauling, 1958). These crystal structure studies have also provided both evidence of the importance of NH—OC hydrogen bonding and values for the nitrogen-oxygen distance to be expected.

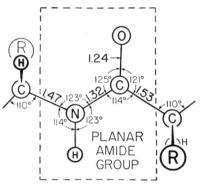

Fig. 1. Fundamental dimensions of polypeptide chains as derived from X-ray crystal analyses of amino acids and simple peptides [Reproduced by permission from Corey, R. B., and Pauling, L., *Rend. ist. lombardo sci. Pt. I* **89**, 10 (1955)].

The first criteria postulated by Pauling, Corey and Branson in the formulation of peptide chain configurations were therefore:

(1). That each peptide chain residue —NH·CH·CO— should have certain precise dimensions without regard to the nature of its side-chain environment.

(2). That the configurations proposed should be stabilized by intra- or interchain hydrogen bonds between the amide C—O and NH groups. The nitrogen-oxygen distance to be equal to 2.79 ± 0.10 A. We shall neglect the interchain hydrogen-bonded β-configurations (appropriate to silk fibroin, β-keratin, etc.) and consider only those configurations dependent upon intrachain hydrogen bonds. Two further criteria were then established.

(3). In the appropriate configuration there should be the maximum possible number of hydrogen bonds and the identical chain residues should all be structurally equivalent. This latter restriction of structural equivalence results in helical configurations. The environment of each peptide chain residue (except, of course, at the two ends of the helix) is the same with respect to adjacent chain residues.

(4). The most probable configurations should have the greatest stability. This requirement may be evaluated in more precise terms; these are discussed in detail elsewhere (Corey and Pauling, 1953; Donohue, 1953).

Whereas the first three criteria are met by several helical configurations (Pauling et al., 1951; Low and Grenville-Wells, 1953), the α-helix alone satisfies the fourth criterion. The α-helix is not simply the most stable backbone polypeptide chain configuration; it is, significantly, the only helical peptide chain configuration with intrachain hydrogen bonds (thus excluding the collagen structure) for which there is any experimental evidence whatsoever. There is abundant evidence that extensive regions of α-helix structure exist in some fibrous proteins, e.g., keratin ("myosin") and considerable evidence that more limited regions of α-helix exist in at least some globular proteins. We may therefore examine this structure more closely (Fig. 2). The drawing shows that each helix residue —C·NH·CO·C— lies in one of a series of planes parallel to the helix axis. The CO and NH groups are very nearly parallel to the helix axis. Each amide group forms hydrogen bonds with the third amide group beyond it in either direction, forming 13-atom loops (Fig. 3). The helix may be represented

$$
\begin{array}{l}
\text{O} \ldots\ldots\ldots\ldots \text{H} \\
\| \qquad\qquad\qquad\quad | \\
\text{C—(NH·CH·CO)}_3\text{—N}
\end{array}
$$

There are 3.6 residues per turn. As the photograph (Fig. 4) shows, the side chains bristle out from the helix core. With the exception of prolyl and hydroxy-prolyl side chains (these are imino acid residues and do not have a free NH group to participate in the helix hydrogen bond formation) the nature of the side-chain group does not stereochemically affect the formation of α-helical structure. A model of the α-helix structure

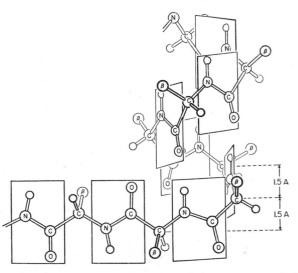

Fig. 2. A drawing showing how the α-helix is generated from the structural elements of the polypeptide chain (the planar amide group and the tetrahedral α-carbon atom) by rotation (100°) around an axis combined with a translation (1.5 A) parallel to the axis [Reproduced by permission from Corey, R. B., and Pauling, L., *Rend. ist. lombardo sci.* *Pt. I* **89**, 10 (1955)].

incorporating any random sequence of amino acid residues may be made without stereochemical hindrance.

The absolute configuration of L-amino acids has been established (Bijvoet *et al.*, 1950). Two α-helix structures may be proposed for any one peptide sequence of L-amino acid residues, a right-handed helix and a left-handed helix. The two are not stereoisomers. The mirror image of a left-handed helix of L-amino acid residues is a right-handed helix of D-amino acid residues. In the α-helix structure the β-carbon position is defined—the other atoms of the side-chain groups have considerable freedom of rotation and may adopt different configurations.

At this point we may consider the α-helix structure in functional terms. Suppose it were known that a region of left-handed or right-handed α-helix existed in some specific region

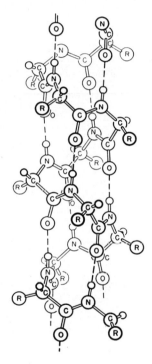

Fig. 3. A drawing of a portion of an α-helix [Reproduced by permission from Corey, R. B., and Pauling, L., *Rend. ist. lombardo sci. Pt. I* **89**, 10 (1955)].

of a protein molecule for which the amino acid sequence had been determined. The relative positions of the backbone chain and β-carbon atoms could then be evaluated precisely.

More pertinently for our discussion, a model could be made. Let us suppose further that there was evidence that the active site of the protein resided somewhere within this region and that we wished to investigate the probable nature of the active site-substrate interaction. Scale models of the α-helix, with side-chain residues attached in appropriate sequence, and of the substrate molecule could be made. If there were any evidence concerning the probable chemical nature of the protein, we might attempt to fit the substrate molecular model over the

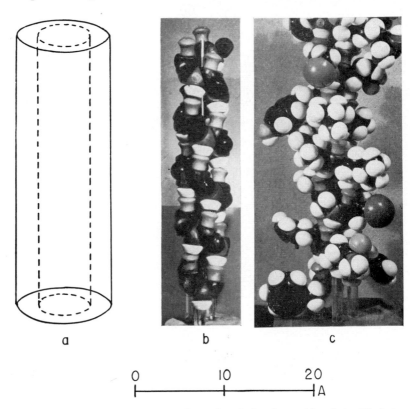

FIG. 4. (a). Cylindrical outline of coiled polypeptide chain 10 A in diameter showing ~5 A backbone chain "core." (b). Model of core of polypeptide chain (—CO·NH·CH—)$_n$ in Pauling-Corey α-helix. (c). Polypeptide chain as (b) with side chains attached (Reproduced by permission from Low, B. W. *In* "The Proteins" (H. Neurath and K. Bailey, eds.), Vol. 1, Part A, Chapter 4, Academic Press, New York, 1953).

α-helix model in the search for an appropriate site.[1] If we had such a problem and if our hypothesis concerning the detailed nature of the active site-substrate interaction were correct, we might well find such a model study most illuminating. At best it would be a limited and profitable exercise akin to the attempt to identify that door in a house which a given key opens by trying to fit the key in turn into each lock. At worst if we were unaware of, or misinformed concerning, the probable nature of the substrate-protein interaction, it would be comparable to the behavior of an inquisitive child who on finding a key, deduced that it fitted into some cavity but could only try all possible cavities, being unaware of the key-keyhole relationship.

Model studies of the former controlled type have been made. To date these have been largely conjectural. That is, the control has been provided by hypothesis rather than evidence. They have been no less valuable and illuminating because of this.

One example of this type of model study is the work of Ehrenberg and Theorell (1955) on the hemopeptide of cytochrome c. The sequence in this peptide has been determined (Tuppy and Paléus, 1955):

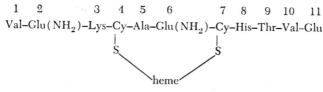

Using scale models of the peptide chain (and the heme group) the authors made models of several helical configurations including both the left- and right-handed α-helix with 3.7 residues per turn. They then tried "to connect the two cysteine side chains of the peptide with the α-carbon atom of the vinyl groups in positions 2 and 4 of the haem disk (two possibilities) and

---

[1] The beautiful work of Dr. I. Wilson (this volume, page 163) is the first example of the successful experimental employment of those principles which imply specific stereochemical relationships between reactants and the active site on an enzyme.

one or two haemochromogen-forming groups with the iron."
Ehrenberg and Theorell were particularly interested in the
haemochromogen-forming capacity of the histidine imidazoles.
Only with α-helix structure were they able to connect the
cysteine (4) to the side chain 4 of the heme disk to give a rigid
but strainless structure with the helix axes very nearly parallel
to both the heme plane and the imidazole plane. They comment
"The α-helix of the haemo peptide occupies just one-quarter of
the space around the haem. In cytochrome c at about neutral
pH it is thus plausible to imagine four such helices arranged
symmetrically about the haem disk, thus shielding it from direct
contact with, for example, oxygen, carbon monoxide or cyanide,
but, nevertheless in some way allowing electrons to be exchanged." Ehrenberg and Theorell then presented experimental
evidence for the view that the iron-linked groups of cytochrome
c are in fact histidine imidazoles.

A further example of such model building studies may be
considered. Once the complete two-dimensional structure of
the insulin molecule was established by Sanger and his co-
workers (1955), the question then arose: Can the A-chain of
insulin (Fig. 5) be coiled into a continuous α-helix structure in
spite of the intrachain cystine disulfide bond between residue 6
and residue 11? A model study quickly provided the answer—
no, it can not. A further question was then posed by several
investigators. What sort of model structures for insulin can be

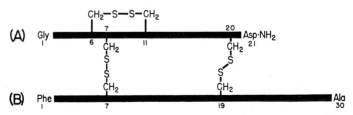

FIG. 5. Outline of the structure of beef, hog, and sheep insulins. The
glycyl (A) chain, with 21 residues, and the phenylalanyl (B) chain, with
30 residues, both have the same orientation, with the free terminal α-amino
groups at the left-hand side of the diagram (Reproduced by permission
from Low, B. W. and Edsall, J. T. *In* "Currents in Biochemical Research" (D. E. Green, ed.), p. 378. Interscience, New York, 1956.)

built if we postulate that the model should have the maximum possible α-helix content? Three different models have been postulated (Lindley and Rollett, 1955; Linderstrøm-Lang, 1955; and Low, 1955). The Lindley and Rollett model is in detail the most satisfying solution to this simple stereochemical inquiry. None of these model structures may necessarily be pertinent to the actual molecular architecture of the proteins investigated. They do certainly provide most illuminating information. It is moreover information which could not be gained without precise formulation of the structure under investigation.

It is, of course, possible that the residue dimension of the helix may in specific cases differ somewhat from those proposed by Pauling and Corey. The side-chain group interaction may cause some variation from residue to residue. Equally, the helix may be wrapped up more or less tightly. Minor changes in the wrap-up angle may alter the helix from one with 3.6 to one with 3.7 residues per turn. In general the effects of such changes will be relatively trivial, except in those cases where different parts of the active site are separated by relatively large distances. For example, the difference between a 3.6 and 3.7 helix will substantially effect the stereochemical relationship between the nth and the $n + 15$th or $n + 16$th residue.

Model studies of this kind serve also to emphasize that the amino acid residue sequence enumerated sequentially does not immediately illuminate the spatial relationships between side-chain groups on an α-helix. The nth side-chain group approaches more closely to the $n + 3$rd and $n + 4$th side-chain group than it does to the $n + 2$nd side-chain group. It would be interesting to examine the known sequences of protein and peptide fragments not simply in order to determine whether or not there are common simple sequences of side-chain groups, but also whether or not there may be common sequences with irregular spacing, for example, n, $n + 1$, $n + 3$, $n + 4$.

There is evidence that there are regions of α-helix in some globular proteins. There is even more persuasive evidence that most globular proteins cannot be described solely in terms of the α-helix structure alone. That is, no protein so far studied appears to be made up solely of one or more peptide chains each coiled along its entire length into one single continuous α-helical array. In several instances the evidence is not derived simply from the comparative study of the size and shape of the molecule and the number of known peptide chains. For example, in the insulin structure one can show that the positions of the intrachain disulfide groups must inhibit α-helix formation in one region of the chain. This restriction applies even more sharply in the ribonuclease molecule (see Anfinsen, 1958; and Hirs *et al.*, 1958).

We may modify the postulates concerning α-helix content to conform with the evidence concerning size and shape. This would provide a model in which regions of α-helix would be succeeded by non-α-helical regions in a manner suggested in Fig. 6. Only three short α-helical regions all lying approxi-

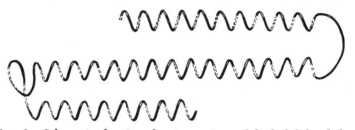

FIG. 6. Schematic drawing showing regions of both left-handed and right-handed α-helix interrupted by loops of nonhelical configuration.

mately in one layer are shown in the figure. A drawing showing more extensive helical and nonhelical regions in a three-dimensional array would be more appropriate to suggest the model we propose. It would be more difficult to draw. For the sake of simplicity the drawing shows parallel regions of α-helix; we do not however imply that this should be a fundamental feature of such a modified model. The parallel packing of regions of helices stacked in close-packed array has been considered in some model studies. This specific type of packing has been invoked not only because of the relationships it suggests between fibrous and globular proteins, but also as a consequence of experimental evidence concerning protein structure. Thus, for example, in the hemoglobin structure studies, Perutz' discovery (1951) of the experimental evidence for the regions of α-helix in hemoglobin depended initially on his assumption that these would be largely parallel, and provides evidence in support of this conclusion. Even in hemoglobin, however, a model of the kind shown in Fig. 6 appears invalid if we assume (a) that the loops which fold back the region of helix into a relatively compact array are fairly short compared to the helical regions they separate, and (b) that the helical regions have the maximum possible length. Bragg et al. (1952) and Crick (1952) have shown that the regions of α-helix in hemoglobin must be either more limited in length and interrupted by numerous discontinuities, or that there is relatively poor alignment of short regions of α-helix in the molecule.

So far, we have considered protein structure in terms of the α-helix alone. The experimental evidence appears to suggest that in the globular protein molecules studied, and these are only a small fraction of the total, there may be some regions of α-helix and other nonhelical regions. This general conclusion, now fairly widely accepted, does not imply that there are regions of α-helix in all globular proteins nor that the percentage of α-helical content may not vary widely from protein to protein. We may tentatively assume that the specific molecular configuration of a protein depends on the amino acid sequence and the consequent interchain packing. (This assumption ignores the possibility that the configuration of the native protein is to some extent "built in" during protein synthesis, and that it would not arise if the synthesis were carried out in another way.) Since both regions of α-helix and non-α-helical regions appear to exist in some proteins, we may suppose that certain amino acid sequences favor and others inhibit α-helix formation. The α-helix configuration is inhibited by certain specific intrachain cystine disulfide linkages and by prolyl and hydroxy-prolyl groups. Such possibilities of simple stereochemical inhibition are inadequate to explain the experimental results.

Kendrew and his associates (1958) have recently described their partial determination of the structure of the myoglobin molecule. The electron density distribution within the crystal is not completely resolved. It is not therefore possible to distinguish atoms. The electron density distribution within the confines of a single molecule has been broadly classified into two regions, one of high electron density and one of relatively low electron density. Although the choice of boundary between the two regions is necessarily somewhat arbitrary, its exact value is not of prime importance to a study of the electron density distribution.

Kendrew and his associates have prepared a scale model of the myoglobin molecule in which the regions of high electron density are enclosed within a solid figure. Figures 7a and 7b show two views of their model. They describe the model and comment on its significance as follows:

"Several points must be noticed. First, the model shows only the general distribution of dense regions. The core of a helical polypeptide chain would be such a region; but if the chain were pulled out, into a β-configuration, for example, its mean density would drop to near the average for the cell and the chain would fade out at this resolution. Similarly, side-chains should, in general, scarcely show up, so that the polypeptide rods in the model must be imagined as clothed in an invisible integument of side-chains, so thick that neighbouring chains in reality touch. Third, features other than polypeptide chains may be responsible for some of the regions of high density; patches of adsorbed salt, for example. Fourth, the surface chosen to demarcate a molecule cannot be traced everywhere with certainty, so it is possible that the molecule shown contains parts of its neighbours, and correspondingly lacks part of its own substance.

"Making due allowance for these difficulties, we may note the main features. It is known (Schmid, K., *Helv. Chim. Acta*,

FIGS. 7a and 7b. Photographs of a model of the myoglobin molecule. Polypeptide chains are white; the gray disk is the heme group. The marks on the scale are 1 A apart. [Reproduced by permission from Kendrew, J. C., Bodo, G., Dintzis, H. M., Parrish, R. G., Wyckoff, H., and Phillips, D. C., *Nature* 181, 662 (1958)].

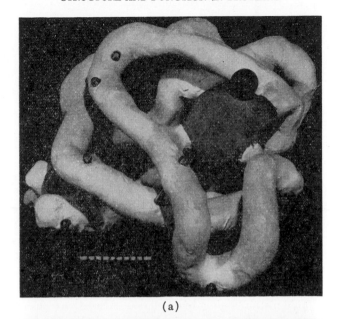

(a)

(b)

32, 105, 1949; Ingram, V. M., unpublished work) that myoglobin has only one terminal amino-group; it is simplest to suppose that it consists of a single polypeptide chain. This chain is folded to form a flat disk of dimensions about 43 A. $\times$ 35 A. $\times$ 23 A. Within the disk chains pursue a complicated course, turning through large angles and generally behaving so irregularly that it is difficult to describe the arrangement in simple terms; but we note the strong tendency for neighboring chains to lie 8–10 A. apart in spite of the irregularity. One might loosely say that the molecule consists of two layers of chains, the predominant directions of which are nearly at right angles in the two layers. If we attempt to trace a single continuous chain throughout the model, we soon run into difficulties and ambiguities, because we must follow it around corners, and it is precisely at corners that the chain must lose the tightly packed configuration which alone makes it visible at this resolution (an α-helix, for example, cannot turn corners without its helical configuration being disrupted). Also, there are several apparent bridges between neighbouring chains, perhaps due to the apposition of bulky side-chains. The model is certainly compatible with a single continuous chain, but there are at least two alternative ways of tracing it through the molecule, and it will not be possible to ascertain which (if either) is correct until the resolution has been improved. Of the secondary structure we can see virtually nothing directly at this stage. Owing to the corners, the chain cannot be in helical configuration throughout; in fact, the total length of chain in the model is 300 A., whereas an α-helix of 152 residues would be only 228 A. long. The 300 A. might correspond, for example, to 70 per cent α-helix and 30 per cent fully extended chain, but of course intermediate configurations are probably present, too. The haem group is held in the structure by links to at least four neighbouring chains; nevertheless, one side of it is readily accessible from the environment to oxygen. . . . Clearly, however, the model cannot at present be correlated in detail with what we know of the chemistry of myoglobin; this must await further refinement."

The *primary structure* of a protein is now usually defined as the precise amino acid sequence along the peptide chains. It is that structure which may be completely represented by a two-dimensional formula.

The *secondary structure* of a protein describes the particular backbone chain configurations which may be found in the protein. Thus, in hemoglobin as discussed earlier the α-helix configuration appears to be one component of the secondary structure. At the third level of organization—the *tertiary structure*—we must consider all the folds and turns which occur in coiled or uncoiled parts of the peptide chain in order to fit the entire molecule into a region of appropriate size and shape.

The study of Kendrew and his associates, an outstanding triumph of structure analysis, provides a picture of the *tertiary structure* of a protein molecule.

In those proteins with inter- or intrachain cystine disulfide linkages, the tertiary structure is dependent to a greater or lesser extent upon these linkages. Indeed, it is possible that certain such loops such as that found in insulin, oxytocin, and vasopressin (see du Vigneaud *et al.*, 1953, 1954) and formed by intrachain cystine disulfide linkages (Fig. 8) may have a well-defined configuration independent of the nature of the side-chain residues whether those of the ring itself or of adjacent regions of the chain.

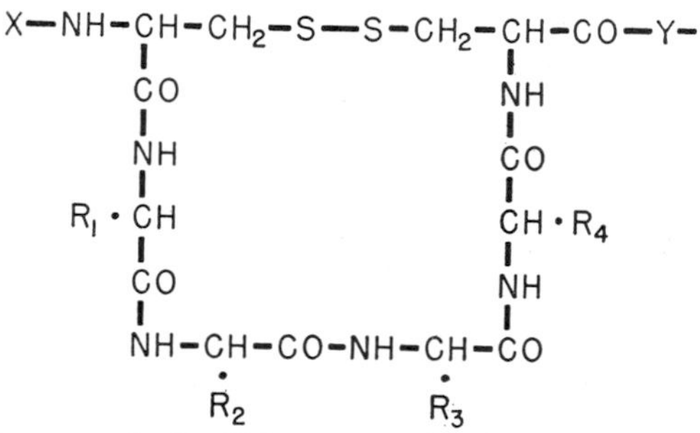
X—NH-CH-CH2-S—S-CH2-CH-CO—Y-
CO
NH
NH
CO
R1 • CH
CH • R4
CO
NH
NH-CH-CO-NH-CH-CO
R2
R3

FIG. 8. The peptide-disulfide ring structure of oxytocin, vasopressin, and insulin. X, Y, R_1, R_2, R_3, and R_4 indicate the positions of the attached groups. (Reproduced by permission from Low, B. W. and Edsall, J. T. *In* "Currents in Biochemical Research" (D. E. Green, ed.), p. 378. Interscience, New York, 1956.)

We are not concerned here with the specific role of the side-chain interactions which may serve to maintain a given molecular configuration. These are discussed in detail elsewhere (see, for example, Low and Edsall, 1956). We should note, however, that without such noncovalent bonds between chains the specific molecular configuration would not be maintained intact if it should have a structure of the kind implied by the model we have adopted. The backbone intrachain hydrogen bonds which are involved in regions of α-helix do not hold successive regions of α-helix in fixed positions relative to each other. From the examination of the type of model structure we have discussed, it becomes obvious that the primary active site of a molecule may have a structure more complex than any presented by the surface of a single α-helix with side chains bristling outward. It may be a composite site formed by the side chains from parts of a molecule far removed from each other in sequence. And, in molecules made up of more than one peptide chain, the conformation of the site may depend on side chains from different chains. (We may note in passing that when disulfide bond positions are established, they provide, in effect, new crossover sequences.)

In discussing this whole question of molecular configuration, of tertiary structure, we have tacitly implied that it is completely definable. That is, that there is one answer to the question—what is the molecular architecture of a certain protein molecule? This is not necessarily true. Indeed, Tanford (1958) has presented evidence that suggests very strongly that in certain proteins there may be major changes in configuration as a result of changes in pH. Until we know more about the details of all the conditions which provoke such changes *in vitro*, we can only speculate about their relevance to the consideration of protein function *in vivo*. We shall therefore neglect this aspect of protein structure with the explicit understanding that it may be most unfortunate to do so.

We now turn to speculative consideration of another kind. These speculations are necessarily my own and can only illuminate my own viewpoint. There are rather few facts to be exhibited. We observe that extensive regions of α-helix appear to occur most prominently in the ordered regions of fibrous proteins, notably α-keratin. One principal function of these proteins appears to be architectural support or some specialized mechanical flexibility. The α-helix structure appears most admirably to meet the needed requirements.

The functions of most globular proteins are not associated primarily with such mechanical requirements. Further, in the globular proteins the stable discrete unit is a single molecule. All the functions of the molecule are confined within the molecular limits. The stability of the molecule in the changing environments through which it may pass from the point of synthesis to the point of interaction must be provided by the molecule alone.

Do the α-helical regions, in molecules in which they occur, provide the active sites whether or not these occur on one helix alone or by interaction between side chains from several such regions? We do not know. I would like to suggest a possible alternative role for the α-helix.

It appears reasonable on chemical and physicochemical grounds to suppose that certain regions of globular molecules are stereochemically inaccessible to molecules and ions found in the aqueous media in which the protein is suspended. If we tentatively assume that, in general, the whole protein molecule is important to proper *in vivo* function, that no large part of the molecule is vestigial, we may then speculate concerning the function of the inaccessible "core."

Regions of α-helix, when they are found in globular proteins, probably make an important contribution to the over-all molecular stability (see Low, 1957 for further discussion). Those regions of a molecule not normally accessible to physiological reagents may provide stability for the molecule as a whole. α-Helices would be excellent for this purpose. Thus, it may be that the function of α-helical regions in globular proteins may be architectural—to stabilize and maintain the special conformation of the active site which may reside in nonhelical regions of the chain.

In the muscle complex there are many different proteins. No one particular protein must necessarily provide both the over-all configurational stability of the complex and the active site. Professor Hans H. Weber has pointed out[2] that the light and heavy meromyosins provide an interesting comment on the possible role of the α-helix, tentatively suggested above. Nekhorocheff et al. (1954) have shown that only H-meromyosin has adenosinetriphosphatase activity. H-Meromyosin appears to have only 45% helical content. L-Meromyosin, on the other hand, appears to contain 74% α-helical content (A. G. Szent-Györgyi and C. Cohen 1957).

These speculations may be totally in error. They may serve simply to emphasize the difficulty in defining the whole problem of relevance in the discussion of any one specific aspect of protein structure.

Happily, this paper is totally different from one which could have been written about protein stereochemistry a decade ago. The critical description of the α-helix has provided new insight into the problem of protein structure and provoked the most vigorous experimental study of this problem by a wide variety of new techniques. The partial structure determination of myoglobin, a magnificent achievement, provides the first direct evidence concerning the nature of the tertiary structure of a globular protein.

Whatever the nature of the precise relationship between structure and function in any one instance, we may now discuss it in more clearly defined molecular stereochemical terms.

REFERENCES

Anfinsen, C. B. In "Symposium on Protein Structure (Intern. Union Pure and Appl. Chem., Paris, 1957)," (A. Neuberger, ed.), Wiley, New York, 1958.

Bijvoet, J. M., Peerdeman, A. F., and van Bommel, A. J. Nature 168, 271 (1950).

---

[2] I am indebted to Professor Weber for permission to incorporate these comments into the body of my paper. Professor Weber made these observations during the open discussion after my paper was presented at the Symposium.

Bragg, W. L., Howells, E. R., and Perutz, M. F. *Acta Cryst.* **5**, 136 (1952).

Corey, R. B. and Pauling, L. *Proc. Roy. Soc.* **B141**, 10 (1953).

Crick, F. H. C. *Acta Cryst.* **5**, 381 (1952).

Donohue, J. *Proc. Natl. Acad. Sci. U. S.* **39**, 470 (1953).

du Vigneaud, V., Lawler, H. C., and Popenoe, E. A. *J. Am. Chem. Soc.* **75**, 4880 (1953).

du Vigneaud, V., Ressler, C., Swan, J.M., Roberts, C. W., and Katsoyannis, P. G. *J. Am. Chem. Soc.* **76**, 3115 (1954).

Ehrenberg, A. and Theorell, H. *Nature* **176**, 158 (1955).

Hirs, C. H. W., Stein, W. H., and Moore, S. *In* "Symposium on Protein Structure (Intern. Union Pure and Appl. Chem., Paris, 1957)," (A. Neuberger, ed.), Wiley, New York, 1958.

Kendrew, J. C., Bodo, G., Dintzis, H. M., Parrish, R. G., Wyckoff, H., and Phillips, D. C. *Nature* **181**, 662 (1958).

Linderstrøm-Lang, K. *In* "Peptide Chemistry: Report of a Symposium held by the Chemical Society, March 30, 1955." The Chemical Society, London; Hvidt, A. and Linderstrøm-Lang, K. *Compt. rend. trav. lab. Carlsberg. Ser. chim.* **29**, 385 (1955).

Lindley, H. and Rollett, J. S. *Biochim. et Biophys. Acta* **18**, 183 (1955).

Low, B. W. (1955). Cited *in* Low, B. W. and Edsall, J. T. "Currents in Biochemical Research" (D. E. Green, ed.). Interscience, New York, 1956.

Low, B. W. *In* "The Chemical Basis of Heredity" (W. D. McElroy and Bentley Glass, eds.). Johns Hopkins Press, Baltimore, Maryland, 1957.

Low, B. W. and Edsall, J. T. *In* "Currents in Biochemical Research" (D. E. Green, ed.). Interscience, New York, 1956.

Low, B. W. and Grenville-Wells, H. J. *Proc. Natl. Acad. Sci. U. S.* **39**, 785 (1953).

Nekhorocheff, J., Dondon, J., and Goussef, Z. *Compt. rend.* **238**, 1450 (1954).

Pauling, L. *In* "Symposium on Protein Structure (Intern. Union Pure and Appl. Chem., Paris, 1957)" (A. Neuberger, ed.). Wiley, New York, 1958.

Pauling, L., Corey, R. B., and Branson, H. R. *Proc. Natl. Acad. Sci. U. S.* **37**, 205 (1951).

Perutz, M. F. *Nature* **167**, 1053 (1951).

Sanger, F. *Bull. soc. chim. biol.* **37**, 23 (1955).

Szent-Györgyi, A. G., and Cohen, C. *Science* **126**, 697 (1957).

Tanford, C. *In* "Symposium on Protein Structure (Intern. Union Pure and Appl. Chem., Paris, 1957)" (A. Neuberger, ed.). Wiley, New York, 1958.

Tuppy, H. and Paléus, S. *Acta Chem. Scand.* **9**, 353 (1955).

Nature and Function of Mucopolysaccharides of Connective Tissue

KARL MEYER

Department of Medicine, Columbia University, College of Physicians and Surgeons, and the Edward Daniels Faulkner Arthritis Clinic of the Presbyterian Hospital, New York

Muscle and nervous tissues like many other tissues and organs contain a considerable portion of connective tissue. Aside from its purely mechanical function as supporting and insulating structure, it may be assumed to play, in muscle and nervous tissues, a regulatory role similar to that which it plays in epithelial tissue and its supporting stroma—a role which suggests itself especially in peripheral nerve. To the biologist interested in chemical structure and biological function, the mucopolysaccharides of connective tissue ought to be of interest, since they probably represent one of the most primitive and most simple of the high polymers in which regularly repeating anionic groups give rise to an astonishing variety of compounds with distinct chemical, physical, and biological properties.

The mucopolysaccharides of connective tissues are generally assumed to be localized in the so-called amorphous ground and cement substances—terms based on light microscopic observations of connective tissues. By electron microscopic methods, these ground and cement substances appear to be amorphous, or are depicted as sheaths or fine fibrils devoid of any apparent fine structure between the collagen bundles. In reticulum, elastic fibers, and glassy membranes, the presence of nonstructured ground substance or of acid mucopolysaccharides has also been demonstrated by histological methods.

In the last 25 years, a systematic investigation of the acid mucopolysaccharides has been carried out in this laboratory. Three facts have become apparent during these studies.

(1). Connective tissue contains a considerable number of chemically related but distinct mucopolysaccharides.

(2). They occur in defined patterns in various tissues.
(3). They are all polyanions.

The acid mucopolysaccharides can be classified into three main groups (Table I).

TABLE I
TYPES OF ACID MUCOPOLYSACCHARIDES

Group I.	Polyuronic acids
	a. Hyaluronic acid
	b. Chondroitin
Group II.	Polyuronic acids—polysulfates
	a. Chondroitin sulfate A, B, and C
	b. Heparitin sulfate
Group III.	Polysulfate
	a. Keratosulfate

Group I consists of only two members—hyaluronic acid and chondroitin, the galactosamine isomer of hyaluronic acid. In contrast to hyaluronic acid, chondroitin contains approximately 2% of ester sulfate (approximately 11% of the amount calculated for the fully sulfated compound). Chondroitin has been isolated only from bovine cornea (1). In aqueous solutions, it has a considerable viscosity and it forms a mucin clot similar to that of hyaluronic acid. These properties distinguish the native chondroitin from the chondroitin sulfates (ChS), and from the compounds prepared by chemical desulfation from ChS A or C. Hyaluronic acid is an almost universal component of connective tissue. In contrast to chondroitin sulfate, neither isomers nor sulfated forms of hyaluronic acid have been encountered—a noteworthy fact, especially in view of the occurrence in most tissues of hyaluronic acid in the presence of various sulfated polysaccharides.

In Group II, the largest number of variations of acidic polymers is encountered. Besides the three chondroitin sulfates listed in Table I, designated as A, B, and C, other variants of these compounds have been encountered, in which either sulfate groups are missing (2) or in which proportions of D-glucuronyl are replaced by their 5-epimer L-iduronyl (3). The fundamental repeating units of the chondroitin sulfates are β1 → 3 hexuronyl N-acetylgalactosamine polymerized to unbranched chains via β1 → 4 hexosaminyl bonds (4). In A and B, sulfation occurs on carbon 4 of the galactosamine, in C on carbon 6 (5). Figure 1 summarizes the structure of the main chondroitin sulfates and, for comparison, that of hyaluronic acid.

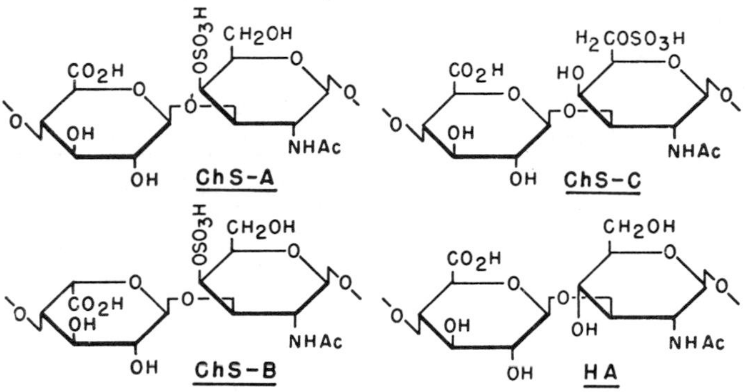

Fig. 1. Structure of the chondroitin sulfates and hyaluronic acid (ChS = chondroitin sulfate; HA = hyaluronic acid). (*Federation Proc.* **17**, 1078, 1958).

The structure of heparitin sulfate is still unknown. It is composed of D-glucosamine and D-glucuronic acid apparently in equimolar proportions. Only half of the glucosamine is N-acetylated, the other half is N-sulfated (6). The composition, the positive optical rotation, and the presence of N-sulfate, point to a close chemical similarity to heparin, a similarity further indicated by their hydrolysis by enzymes obtained from microorganisms adapted either to heparin or to heparitin sulfate (7). From the sulfate content and from data on the liberation of sulfate by mild acid hydrolysis, it is apparent that heparitin sulfate contains at most one-half of the sulfate groups as O-sulfate.

In Group III, only one representative is known, keratosulfate, a polymer of unknown structure composed of equimolar quantities of N-acetylglucosamine, D-galactose, and sulfate, i.e., sulfate is its only repeating anionic group (8). Whether keratosulfate as isolated from different sources, i.e., from cornea (8), nucleus pulposus (9), calf bone (2), or human cartilage (10), is identical or not cannot be decided at present.

The sites of biosynthesis of the acid mucopolysaccharides appear to be the various connective tissue cells. This has been concluded from the production of hyaluronic acid and chondroitin sulfate(s) in tissue cultures of fibroblasts originating from subcutaneous tissue, bone, or synovial cells (11). We further assume that these cells in various sites differentiate, so that each type will produce only one specific polysaccharide. This may be concluded, for example, from the distribution of the mucopolysaccharides in different connective tissues, and the occurrence of only one type of polysaccharide, either hyaluronic acid, or ChS A or C, in different mesenchymal tumors (see below).

In normal connective tissue, usually three or more polysaccharides occur in proportions which appear to be typical for the mature tissues. These ratios vary, however, with the age of the species. Examples of such changes with age have been described in pig skin where in the adult the ratio of ChS B to hyaluronate is 1.25 while in the embryo and newborn the ratio is 0.20 or less (12). Apparently in other embryonic tissues, ChS B is either absent or in very low concentrations. The most striking age changes of the mucopolysaccharides have been observed in human rib cartilage. In the newborn, this tissue contains a high concentration of chondroitin sulfate which proved to be almost all 4-sulfate (A). With increasing age, the chondroitin sulfate content decreases steadily while keratosulfate increases from the first year to adulthood and then remains steady. Furthermore, in the adult, Ch-4-S is practically all replaced by Ch-6-S (C) (10, 13). In general, embryonic tissue or rapidly growing tissue has a far higher mucopolysaccharide content than adult or aging tissues.

Considerable efforts have been devoted to the elucidation of the dimensions and shape of isolated mucopolysaccharides in aqueous solutions. The molecular weight of hyaluronate of different origin has been estimated as varying between 20,000 and 10,000,000 (*14*), that of different chondroitin sulfates as between 19,000 and 50,000 (*15*). Both are said to behave as random coils in solution. The question has to be asked what the shape of these molecules is in the tissues. There is little doubt about the intimate association in connective tissues between the structured proteins and the polysaccharides or their protein complexes. In embryonic development, in wound healing, and in other biological processes of fiber formation, the latter is either preceded or concomitant with the elaboration of acid mucopolysaccharides. As a rule, in embryonal tissues as well as in wound healing or in callus formation, it seems that first hyaluronic acid is elaborated, followed by sulfated polysaccharides. Hyaluronic acid is found in high concentration in some primitive mesenchymal tissues as in Wharton's jelly of the umbilical cord, in the coxcomb, especially after stimulation by androgens (*16*), in superficial layers of mammalian skin in the young, and in the loose connective tissue of the electric organ of torpedo (*17*). In all these tissues, it always occurs accompanied by a chondroitin 6-sulfate (C). Hyaluronic acid further occurs in elastic tissue, i.e., in ligamentum nuchae and aorta (*18*). Indeed, it appears that the various sulfated polysaccharides are associated with collagenous fibers of different histological appearance. Thus, ChS C appears in conjunction with fine immature collagen fibers and ChS B with the coarse fiber bundles of mature tissue. It may be surmised that the architecture of the collagen bundles is determined by the type of mucopolysaccharide elaborated by the fibrocytes in the various types of connective tissues, or, in other words, that fibrous proteins as well as the various types of mucopolysaccharides are manifestations of the differentiation of fibroblasts into specific cells of the connective tissue. In accordance with this hypothesis is the finding that in tumors of connective tissues only one type of mucopolysaccharide has been encountered. Thus, from Rous sarcoma, a human liposarcoma, a synovioma and mesothelioma, only hyaluronic acid was obtained while chondrosarcoma and a chordoma yielded only ChS C and one chondrosarcoma ChS A. It further can be expected, that in malformations of the connective tissues, the pattern of muco-polysaccharides would be altered. At present, only in one systemic disease of connective tissue have abnormal patterns of mucopolysaccharides been established—in Hurler's syndrome. In this inherited disease, ChS B and heparitin sulfate are stored intracellularly in various tissues in large quantities, even in tissues which normally do not contain demonstrable quantities of these polysaccharides. Concomitant with their accumulation in tissue cells, these polysaccharides are excreted in large quantities in the urine, where in most cases the concentration of ChS B is twice that of heparitin sulfate (19).

In organs, however, the proportions of the polysaccharides vary: the liver contains very large quantities (up to 8% of the defatted dry weight) of heparitin sulfate together with only small quantities of ChS B, while in the spleen and brain ChS B predominates over heparitin sulfate. Apparently, in Hurler's syndrome the two mucopolysaccharides are produced and excreted in excess and stored in various mesenchymal and parenchymal cells. It is not known which cells produce and which acquire the polysaccharides from blood and other surrounding fluids. The genetic defect underlying the disease is obscure, but some, if not all, the manifestations are undoubtedly caused by the substitution of the mucopolysaccharides normal for the tissues, by substances not normally present.

An analysis of the biological functions of the mucopolysaccharides has to be based on their known chemical and physical properties, on their distribution and biological changes in the tissues, and on correlations with other tissue components. From the chemical data described above, it seems obvious that the most distinct property of the mucopolysaccharides is their anionic character. In fact, the regularity of the repeating units, and the variation of the type and distance from each other of the anionic groups found in these compounds, suggest that they act as templates or organizers in the development of the architecture of the organized fibrous elements of the connective tissues. In accordance with this hypothesis is the correlation of coarseness of the collagenous fibers with the presence of

ChS B and its absence in tissues possessing fine collagen fibers. According to this hypothesis, the collagens of different tissues will be expected to be chemically distinct, and to possess basic regions in register with the anionic groups of the mucopolysaccharides. It might be further expected that such corresponding periodic regions would possess a high degree of orientation in contrast to the random coiling of the isolated polysaccharides in solution. Orientation of mucopolysaccharide has been postulated recently in elastic fibers of ligamentum nuchae and aorta, based on studies by polarized light microscopy and staining reactions before and after enzymatic digestion with testicular hyaluronidase (20). It was concluded from these studies that hyaluronic acid had an orientation identical with that of the elastic fibers. It should be pointed out, however, that the data do not permit a distinction in these experiments between hyaluronic acid and chondroitin sulfate, both of which are present in these elastic tissues. In fact, Ch-4-S (A) is the main polysaccharide fraction of aorta; in young bovine aorta, it constitutes approximately 45% of the total mucopolysaccharide fraction while the hyaluronic acid fraction is 23%. In ligamentum nuchae, ChS A and hyaluronic acid contribute 25% each, and ChS B contributes 50% of the total mucopolysaccharides. In the top layer of bovine skin which contained the elastic fibers, hyaluronic acid is the main polysaccharide fraction. Thus it appears that hyaluronic acid is a component of the elastic fibers, and may contribute to their elastic properties by permitting the elastic fibers to glide or slip over against the relatively rigid collagen fibers interwoven into the elastic tissue. In other tissues, as well as in synovial fluid, the main function of hyaluronic acid appears to be its water-binding property and its function as a shock absorber and lubricant.

It may be expected that the rapidly developing techniques of electron microscope histology, studies on abnormalities of connective tissue, and experimental embryology will permit the analysis of the location, orientation, and biological functions of the acid mucopolysaccharides of connective tissues.

REFERENCES

1. Davidson, E. A., and Meyer, K. *J. Biol. Chem.* **211**, 605 (1954).
2. Meyer, K. *Ciba Foundation Symposium. Bone Structure and Metabolism* p. 65 (1956).
3. Hoffman, P., Linker, A., and Meyer, K. *Arch. Biochem. Biophys.* **69**, 435 (1957).
4. Hoffman, P., Linker, A., and Meyer, K. *Federation Proc.* **17**, 1078 (1958).
5. Hoffman, P., Linker, A., and Meyer, K. *Biochim. et Biophys. Acta* **30**, 184 (1958).
6. Linker, A., Hoffman, P., Sampson, P., and Meyer, K. *Biochim. et Biophys. Acta* **29**, 443 (1958).
7. Hoffman, P., Linker, A., Sampson, P., Meyer, K., and Korn, E. D. *Biochim. et Biophys. Acta* **25**, 658 (1957).
8. Meyer, K., Linker, A., Davidson, E. A., and Weissmann, B. *J. Biol. Chem.* **205**, 611 (1953).
9. Gardell, S. *Acta Chem. Scand.* **9**, 1035 (1955).
10. Meyer, K., Hoffman, P., and Linker, A. *Science* **128**, 896 (1958).
11. Grossfeld, H., Meyer, K., Godman, G., and Linker, A. *J. Biophys. Biochem. Cytol.* **3**, 391 (1957).
12. Loewi, G., and Meyer, K. *Biochim. et Biophys. Acta* **27**, 453 (1958).
13. Kaplan, D., and Meyer, K. *Nature* **183**, 1267 (1959).
14. Balazs, E. A. *Federation Proc.* **17**, 1086 (1958).
15. Mathews, M. B. *Arch. Biochem. Biophys.* **61**, 367 (1956).
16. Schiller, S., Benditt, E. P., and Dorfman, A. *Endocrinology* **50**, 504 (1952).
17. Meyer, K., Davidson, E. A., Linker, A., and Hoffman, P. *Biochim. et Biophys. Acta* **21**, 506 (1956).
18. Meyer, K., Hoffman, P., and Linker, A. *In* "Connective Tissue" p. 86. Blackwell, Oxford, 1957.
19. Meyer, K., Hoffman, P., Linker, A., Grumbach, M. M., and Sampson, P. Unpublished data.
20. Romha'nyi, G. *Nature* **182**, 929 (1958).

The Physical Chemistry of Nerve Action

HENRY EYRING

Department of Chemistry, University of Utah, Salt Lake City, Utah

INTRODUCTION

Resting potentials of about a tenth of a volt across membranes of living cells is a readily understood reflection of the concentration gradients set up by the asymmetric distribution of the metabolic enzymes. Such potentials develop to balance the unequal rate of diffusion of ions through the membrane. The rates of diffusion of ions through membranes depend upon the molecules held in the coordination shell of the ion. In fact, a membrane may be expected to exhibit completely different permeabilities to ions solvated with water and to those ions which have one or more of their coordinating water molecules replaced by some hydrophobic metabolite increasing the permeability of the ion through the lipid layer.

POTENTIALS CALCULATED BY REACTION RATE THEORY

Reaction rate theory provides a ready means of writing down the expression for the potential across a membrane. For the current density, I, one can write:

$$I = 96,500 \ \Sigma_i Z_i k''_i \lambda_i (a_i e^{\mu_j Z_j E \, 23,060/RT} - a'_i e^{-(1-\mu_j) Z_j E \, 23,060/RT})$$

$$(1)$$

Here 96,500 is the faraday expressed in coulombs; Z_i is the absolute value of the valence of the ith ion; k_i is the effective rate of passing through the membrane in trips per second; λ_i is the jump distance of the ith ion in the medium adjacent to the membrane; a_i is the activity of the ith ion belonging to the team whose penetration of the barrier constitutes a positive current while the activities of the team carrying current in the opposite direction are indicated by a'_i. In each team the positive ions from one side of the barrier are teamed up with the negative ions from the other side. The passage of an ion through a membrane involves the jumping of the ions from site to site. Consequently the effective rate constant k''_i is in some cases a complicated expression involving the rate constants for the individual jumps, as well as factors expressing the probability that a site is available for occupancy. This latter effect leads to interference of an ion by similar ions, as well as by other ions sufficiently strongly held on the adsorption sites. This result is analogous to poisoning in catalytic reactions. Also, the individual rate constants in k are notably dependent on the potential, E, and on various types of adsorbed molecules including hormones. Such effects alter the membrane structure, and through this the free energy of activation for jumping. Finally, equation (1) expresses a first-order dependence of diffusion on the activity. As in surface reactions, this first-order dependence might change to zero order, or to some other order, as the activity changes. In such cases, k''_i will itself show a dependence on the ion activity.

When sufficient impedance is introduced into the external circuit the current, I, approaches zero and if the electrical asymmetry μ_i may be taken as the same for all ions equation (1) becomes

$$E = \frac{RT}{Z\,23,060}\ln\left\{\frac{\sum_i Z_i k''_i \lambda_i a'_i e^{-(1-\mu_i)(Z_i-Z)E\times23,060/RT}}{\sum_i Z_i k''_i \lambda_i a_i e^{-\mu_i(Z_i-Z)E\times23,060/RT}}\right\} \quad (2)$$

If all ions have the same absolute valence equal to Z, equation (2) reduces to Goldman's equation (1, 2)

$$E = \frac{RT}{Z\,23,060}\ln\left\{\frac{\sum_i Z_i k''_i \lambda_i a'_i}{\sum_i Z_i k''_i \lambda_i a_i}\right\} \quad (3)$$

If a membrane is permeable to but one ion, equation (3) reduces to the familiar Nernst equation

$$E = \frac{RT\,2.303}{Z\,23,060}\log_{10}\frac{a'_i}{a_i} \quad (4)$$

Thus a glass electrode which only allows [H+] ions to pass

measures the relative activities of [H$^+$] ions on the two sides of the glass membrane.

Now the resting potential in a nerve will reflect the ratio of the relative activities on the two sides of the membrane of the most permeable ion if this ion's permeability greatly exceeds all others. If in a living nerve cell some metabolite, P, which complexes strongly with sodium to make a very permeable ion, is buffered at a much higher concentration inside than outside the cell, then the resting potential will approximately be given by equation (4) with a'_i set equal to the activity of (Na P$^+$) on one side of the membrane and a_i equal to the activity of this ion on the other side. If other ions have comparable permeabilities then equation (3) must be used to calculate the resting potential.

When the membrane potential, E, is not given by equation (3) the transient action potential should be calculated using equation (1) where we replace I by making the substitution.

$$I = \frac{\varepsilon}{4\pi d} \frac{dE}{dT} \qquad (5)$$

Here ε is the effective dielectric constant of the membrane in which the charge on the two sides of the membrane is separated by the distance d. Thus we obtain

$$\frac{\varepsilon}{4\pi d} \frac{dE}{dT} =$$

$$96,500 \sum_i Z_i k''_i \lambda_i \left(a_i e^{23,060\mu_i Z_i E/RT} - a'_i e^{-(1-\mu_i)Z_i E\, 23,060} \right) \qquad (6)$$

Parlin and the author (2) have demonstrated the general applicability of equation (6) to action potentials. Closer agreement between theory and experiment for the action potential requires that account be taken of the known dependence of the permeability ($k''_i \lambda_i$) on the time.

THE NATURE OF NERVE MEMBRANES

Hodgkin and Huxley (3) have arrived at a set of equations which give good account of the action potential. The physical meaning of certain of their quantities is of considerable interest.

By using the method of the justly famous voltage clamp (4) which maintains the potential of a nerve at a fixed value, it was found that the time course of reactions determining the permeability of the membrane could be expressed by rate constants which changed only with voltage and temperature. Thus Hodgkin and Huxley solved the equations

$$I = C(dV/dt) + p_K(V—V_K) + p_{Na}(V—V_{Na}) + p_l(V—V_l)$$

$$(7)$$

$$p_{Na} = p^o{}_{Na}m^3h \tag{8}$$

$$p_K = p^o{}_K n^4 \tag{9}$$

$$dm/dt = \alpha_m(1—m) — \beta_m m \tag{10}$$

$$dh/dt = \alpha_h(1—h) — \beta_h h \tag{11}$$

$$dn/dt = \alpha_n(1—n) — \beta_n n \tag{12}$$

They also give equations for the six rate constants α_h, β_h, etc., as functions of the voltage. Here I, C, V, p_K, V_K, p_{Na}, V_{Na}, p_l, V_l, and t are the current density, capacity per square centimeter, potential across the membrane, permeability coefficient for potassium, resting potential for potassium, permeability coefficient for sodium, resting potential for sodium, permeability coefficient for other ions, resting potential for other ions and the time. The letters, n, h, and m, represent the mole fractions of some unspecified substance which determine the permeabilities. The sodium permeability increases fiftyfold to a maximum, and then drops to a small value again as the voltage is clamped at some value below the resting potential as a result of the changes in h and m; whereas n and therefore the permeability of potassium rises to a limiting value characteristic of the imposed potential.

The letter, h, symbolizes the mole fraction of some substance which, like acetylcholine acting on end plates, contributes to sodium permeability. Acetylcholine is also quickly inactivated by hydrolysis by the enzyme cholinesterase much as the substance, h, is eliminated by some unknown agency. Nachmansohn and Wilson's results (5) are interesting because they show the universal presence of acetylcholine and cholinesterase in nerve tissue and in bioelectric organs, and further indicate that acetylcholine when injected into a nerve in which the cholinesterase is inactivated by eserine, stimulates the action potential as substance h would presumably do. Thus, substance h is either acetylcholine or something remarkably like it in its behavior.

The identity of substances m and n are likewise obscure. Since the nerve membrane is composed of proteins and lipids and is made impermeable to ions by the resting potential, it must be that the potential orients the molecules. Such orientation of similar molecules tends to line up in a plane (parallel to the membrane surface) hydrophobic parts of the membrane and bands of positive charge, as well as bands of negative charge. An ion has, therefore, much more difficulty threading its way through such an oriented membrane, for it encounters continuous, almost impassable lipid layers, as well as continuous bands of positive charge impermeable to positive ions, and negative bands impermeable to negative ions. As the resting potential is lowered by polarization, the orientation decreases; the impervious layers are broken up, and the permeability is correspondingly increased. Similarly, if charged ions like acetylcholine are released and dissolve in the membrane, they will tend to form a continuous charged band, since they will have affinity for the same group on neighboring membrane molecules. But the repulsion between the adsorbed positively-charged acetylcholine ions will have a powerful disorienting effect on the membrane, and so tend to make it permeable. Now the effect of drop of membrane potential on the rate constants for change in the mole fractions of the substances, h, m, and n, are as though these substances carried half a dozen charges. This is only difficult to understand if one forgets that the reaction coordinate for a chemical reaction may involve simultaneous changes in the coordinates of many neighboring molecules, especially in a cooperative situation in which an oriented molecule is passing into a disoriented state carrying its neighbors with it. Thus a drop in the orienting potential of a few millivolts can easily appear magnified several fold in the exponential term of the rate constant as it in fact does.

ACTIVE TRANSPORT AND THE RESTING POTENTIAL

We have been considering permeability during the action potential where first sodium ions reach fifty times the resting permeability, only to lose this permeability as the potassium ions proceed to surpass the sodium permeability, and so shift the potential back toward the resting state—finally restoring the original resting potential.

The resting potential is developed as a result of the sodium ion being pumped out of the cell at the same time the potassium ion is pumped into it. The coupling of the pump for the two ions is shown (6) by the fact that (1) reducing extracellular potassium reduces sodium efflux; (2) neither sodium nor potassium nor hydrogen ions are distributed in a way that would correspond to the Nernst potential; (3) digitalis inhibits sodium efflux and potassium influx if put on the outside of the membrane (7, 8); (4) potassium ion antagonizes digitalis more than chloride ion does; (5) all known effective agents, except fluoride ion, which inhibit sodium efflux inhibit potassium influx; (6) fluoride in red cells inhibits Na^+ efflux and greatly enhances K^+ influx and efflux; (7) in the squid axon it is found that (a) 2,4-dinitrophenol DNP reduces Na^+ efflux and K^+ influx by equal absolute amounts; (b) the Q_{10} of Na^+ efflux and K^+ influx is between (3 to 5)—indicating a coupling with the metabolism; (c) the Q_{10} of Na^+ influx and K^+ efflux is about 2—indicating passive diffusion.

It is still difficult to ascertain which pump substance co-ordinates with the Na^+ inside the cell for the outward trip through the membrane, and then, after a chemical reaction coordinates with K^+, pumps the latter ion into the cell. Dougherty and the author (9) have considered the possibility that histidine might sometimes act as this pump substance. The marked biological activities of glutamine, serotonin and aldosterone make it extremely interesting to examine their role in influencing cell membrane permeability.

Asymmetric Membrane Potentials

In equations (1), (2), and (3), the factor $k''_i \lambda_i$ represents the permeability of a membrane if one barrier, having the rate constant, k_i, and the width between barrier tops, λ_i, is rate determining. When a succession of n barriers are of comparable height one has

$$k''_i = (k_1^{-1} + k_2^{-1} + \ldots k_i^{-1} + \ldots k_n^{-1})^{-1} \qquad (13)$$

Here one calculates each k_i (using absolute reaction rate theory) as though the other barriers were of negligible height. If m parallel paths are available across the ith barrier one replaces k_i in equation (13) by the sum $\sum_{j=1}^{m} k_{ij}$. In fact the membrane may be treated as an electric network in which k_i is the ith conductance and hence $1/k_i$ is the ith resistance. An extensive cataloging of the types of networks which membranes exhibit will not be undertaken here. One expects almost every imaginable network complexity will be found to occur in different types of membranes.

Since it has occasioned some surprise that the inward current, M_{in}, and the outward current, M_{out}, for potassium do not always obey the relationship

$$M_{in}/M_{out} = [K_o^+]/[K_i^+]e^{E/RT} \qquad (14)$$

suggested by Ussing (10, 11). This result follows directly from rate theory as long as no blocking substances are present. We will discuss the case where a single barrier in the membrane is rate determining. The result is readily generalized to the case of n successive barriers. Using the Langmuir method for adsorption on the membrane sites outside the cell one has:

$$k_o \sigma_o = [K_o^+]k'_o (1 - \sigma_o) \qquad (15)$$

Here k_o, σ_o, $[K_o^+]$, and k'_o are respectively, the rate constants for desorption of potassium ions from an outside adsorbed site, the fraction of these sites covered, the concentration of potassium ions, and finally the specific rate for adsorption of potassium ions on a vacant site. If one replaces the subscript o for outside by i for inside in equation (15) we have

$$k_i \sigma_i = [K_i^+]k'_i(1 - \sigma_i) \qquad (16)$$

Applying rate theory one obtains

$$M_{in} = \frac{96,500 \times 10^{15}}{6.02 \times 10^{23}} \sigma_0 (1-\sigma_i) \frac{kT}{h} e^{-\Delta F^{\ddagger}/RT} e^{\mu E/RT} \tag{17}$$

and

$$M_{out} = \frac{96,500 \times 10^{15}}{6.02 \times 10^{23}} \sigma_i (1-\sigma_0) \frac{kT}{h} e^{-\Delta F^{\ddagger}/RT} e^{-(1-\mu)E/RT} \tag{18}$$

Combining these last four equations does in fact yield (14). However, if some substance other than potassium fills a fraction, i.e., σ_i of the sites on the outer side of the membrane, one has instead of equation (15) the equation

$$k_0 \sigma_0 = [K_0^+] k'_0 (1-\sigma_i-\sigma_0) \tag{19}$$

which when combined with (16), (17), and (18) yields

$$\frac{M_{in}}{M_{out}} = \frac{(1-\sigma_i)}{(1+[K_0^+]/K)\sigma_i} \frac{[K_0^+]}{[K_i^+]} e^{E/RT} \tag{20}$$

Here $(k_0/k'_0) = K$.

This is an extremely odd but very interesting result. Since at the steady state $M_{in} = M_{out}$ it follows that (20) is quite another equation for the membrane potential than Nernst's, and it is likewise something quite different than the Donnan equation. Thus we see that a substance which blocks adsorption sites asymmetrically on the two sides of a membrane will cause a potential to develop across the resulting asymmetric barrier in much the same way a potential is developed at a boundary between p- and n-type atoms in a transistor. Thus, with an adsorbent on only one side of a membrane, any reaction which changes the fraction, σ_i, of the blocked surface will shift the membrane potential. It will be important to ascertain experimentally what role asymmetric barrier potentials play in nerves and in other membranes. Equation (20) is particularly illuminating in showing how a hormone adsorbed on one side of a membrane can promote absorption or secretion of an ion blocked by the hormone. Equation (20) applies equally well to the ratio of the inward and outward material currents of an unionized substance crossing a membrane, provided E is set equal to zero and the concentrations for the unionized diffusant on the two sides of the membrane replace $[K_i^+]$ and $[K_o^+]$. I hope enough has been said to emphasize the usefulness of the relaxation theory approach to transport problems.

ACKNOWLEDGMENTS

I wish to express my appreciation to Alan R. Koch and J. Walter Woodbury for their helpful suggestions.

REFERENCES

1. Goldman, D. E. *J. Gen. Physiol.* **27**, 37-60, 1943.
2. Parlin, R. B., and Eyring, H. *In* "Ion Transport Across Membranes" (H. T. Clarke, ed.), p. 103. Academic Press, New York, 1954.
3. Hodgkin, A. L., and Huxley, A. F. *J. Physiol.* **117**, 500 (1952).
4. Cole, K. S. *Arch. sci. physiol.* **3**, 253-258 (1949).
5. Nachmansohn, D., and Wilson, I. B. "Electrochemistry in Biology and Medicine" (T. Shedlovsky, ed.), p. 167. Wiley, New York, 1955.
6. Hodgkin, A. L., and Keynes, R. D. *J. Physiol.* **126**, 28-60 (1955).
7. Glynn, I. M. *J. Physiol.* **136**, 148-173 (1957).
8. Paton, W. D. M. *Ann. Rev. Physiol.* **20**, 431 (1958).
9. Eyring, H., and Dougherty, T. *Am. Scientist* **43**, 457-467 (1955).
10. Ussing, H. H. *Acta Physiol. Scand.* **19**, 43-56 (1949).
11. Hodgkin, A. L., and Keynes, R. D. *J. Physiol.* **128**, 61-88 (1955).

The Molecular Biology of Cell Membranes

J. D. ROBERTSON

Department of Anatomy, University College London, England

I. INTRODUCTION

The presence of a boundary between the cytoplasm of cells and the outside has been observed many times by light microscopy. This boundary was shown by Cole (6) to have elastic and cohesive properties which could not be explained adequately by the assumption that only an interfacial film was involved. Furthermore, light microscopists have shown that cell boundaries can be pulled out with micromanipulators in a way suggesting strongly that more than an interfacial film is involved. Although the presence of some definite, organized molecular structure of fairly stable composition (relative to adjacent bulk phases) was implied by such findings, it was not possible to define its structure by light microscopy because of limited resolution. In fact, from time to time doubts have been expressed regarding the reality of any organized cell membrane structure. There are still those who question its existence, and it is possible to argue that many phenomena which have been explained on the basis of a hypothetical membrane, can be explained by other means. Nevertheless, the conception of a definite, organized molecular boundary structure at cell surfaces has become well rooted in both physiological and anatomical literature, and it has recently been possible to define such a structure in morphological terms by electron microscopy (55, 62).

On the basis of permeability studies and experimental observations, Danielli and Davson (9) over twenty years ago, proposed a hypothetical membrane structure consisting of organized layers of lipid and protein. They visualized a membrane consisting of a lipid core; containing at least two, and possibly many more, molecular layers of asymmetric lipid molecules, with their nonpolar chains oriented perpendicular to the surface of the

membrane. The outermost monolayers of lipid were supposed to
have their polar groups oriented away from the center of the
membrane, and associated with tangentially organized, molecularly thin layers of protein as indicated in Text Fig. 1. This con-

EXTERIOR

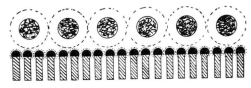

LIPID

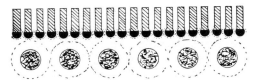

INTERIOR

TEXT FIG. 1.   The model of cell membrane structure proposed by Danielli
and Davson (10). The number of lipid layers is not specified and the protein component diagramed on the outside is visualized as globular
molecules.

ception of membrane structure, was based partly upon the
observations of Overton (47), which suggested that cell membranes contain lipid because of the permeability characteristics
of some cells, and partly upon Langmuir's work on monomolec-
ular lipid films (36). Langmuir demonstrated that lipid molecules, at an air-water interface, arrange themselves in monolayers,
with their nonpolar carbon chains in lateral register perpendicular to the water surface, and their polar groups oriented toward
the water. Subsequently, Gorter and Grendel (30) found that a
mixture of phospholipids could be extracted from red blood
cells and spread in a monolayer. The area of the monolayer
was approximately twice the surface area of the red blood cells
from which the lipids were extracted. They proposed, there-

fore, that the red blood cell membrane consisted of a single bimolecular leaflet of lipid oriented as shown in Text Fig. 2.

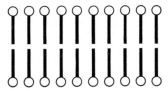

TEXT FIG. 2.   The conception of red cell membrane structure derived from the work of Gorter and Grendel (29). Phospholipid molecules are indicated by the light circles with attached black bars. The circles represent the polar ends of the molecules and the black bars the nonpolar chains.

Danielli and Harvey (10), in studies of lipid inclusions in marine eggs, later concluded that any cytoplasmic lipid layer must be covered by at least one monolayer of protein. This conclusion was reached when they found that the surface tension of intracellular lipid droplets, as measured by a special centrifuge microscope technique, was much lower than could be expected of a pure lipid-water interface. Cole (6) had already measured the surface tension of arbacia eggs and arrived at extremely low values of surface tension, which could not readily be explained on the basis of a pure lipid membrane. Schmitt (69) and Schmitt, Bear and Ponder (74, 75), during the same period, studied the birefringent properties of red blood cells, and concluded that the membrane bounding the cell contained lipid molecules oriented radially. Still later, Waugh and Schmitt (83) measured the thickness of red cell membranes by means of their analytical leptoscope technique, and decided that red cell membranes were in the range of 100 to 200 A in thickness, with 50 to 100 A of the thickness due to lipids. More recent measurements by Waugh (82) gave values of ∼ 40 A for the lipid component. These measurements suggested values of membrane thickness very near those calculated by means of electrical measurements of membrane capacity (7, 8). All of these findings resulted in a conception of cell membrane structure that was embodied in the so-called paucimolecular theory presented by Davson and Danielli (11).

The paucimolecular theory, despite some opposition and some disagreement regarding details, has received wide acceptance. Nevertheless, the matter has remained rather controversial. For example, Mitchison (45) has presented evidence, derived from polarized light studies of red blood cells, suggesting a much more complicated, and much thicker, molecular structure.

The development of electron microscope techniques for the direct observation of cells and tissues as regards details of membrane structure was at first not very informative. Red blood cell membranes, for example, were studied with the electron microscope by direct observation and examination of replicas by Bessis and Bricka (3), Hillier and Hoffman (33), Latta (38), and others [see Ponder (48) for references]. Certain differences in red cell membranes treated in different ways were described. However, it remained for the sectioning techniques to make possible the direct observation of cell membranes in transverse planes. The surface of red cells in thin sections of OsO_4-fixed material showed very little internal structure (2), and it was only with the introduction of new techniques that a consistent layered structure was seen (62) (see below).

In order to observe cell membranes in sections with the electron microscope, it is necessary to alter the structure in some way, to make the cells capable of withstanding the subsequent procedures necessary in the preparation of a section through the membrane. Such procedures involve chemical fixation, dehydration with solvents that may remove lipids, and embedding in a plastic material of sufficient strength and hardness for the preparation of thin sections. The first successful chemical fixative adapted to electron microscopy was OsO_4. Studies of cell membranes after OsO_4 fixation in thin sections were at first inconsistent and somewhat unrewarding. For a time, no consistent internal structure was seen. There was a dense line separating cytoplasm from the outside, and in some cells, further dense layers were observed extending out for a distance of several hundred angstrom units. It was not clear at first what structures should be referred to as the cell membrane, and what structures were of extraneous origin. Indeed, this problem is not yet completely settled. However, some progress has been made, and it now appears possible to define a certain pattern of structure characteristic of cell membranes generally. This results in part from the development of new fixation (potassium permanganate) and embedding techniques (Araldite). Not only has it been possible to define a cell membrane structure, but also to define the structures commonly observed between closely related cells. It is the purpose of this paper to indicate, first of all, the evidence and reasoning involved in arriving at an operational definition of the term "cell membrane" based on electron microscope observations, and secondly, to present evidence regarding cell membranes in nerve fibers, that may be importantly related to nerve impulse propagation and initiation. We shall begin with a general description of certain features of adult nerve fiber structure.

II. Adult Nerve Fiber Structure

It has been known for a long time from classical histological studies that peripheral nerve fibers fall into two major groups— myelinated and unmyelinated. Unmyelinated nerve fibers were thought to consist of closely associated axons and Schwann cells. It appeared that some of the axons were completely contained within syncytial tubes of Schwann cytoplasm. The latter conception was radically revised as a result of the work of Gasser (26– 28). He showed that, in the case of unmyelinated nerve fibers, Schwann cells and axons are, in fact, completely separate, membrane-bounded, entities. The axons are merely embedded in deep troughs in the surfaces of Schwann cells, with a Schwann cell membrane retaining its continuity with the surface, and around the embedded axons as indicated in Text Fig. 3a. The lips of Schwann cytoplasm come together around the embedded axons, and their bounding membranes form a paired membrane structure, which Gasser referred to by the term "mesaxon." He used this term because an analogy could be drawn between the arrangement of an axon and its satellite Schwann cell, and the arrangement of the intestine in the coelom of vertebrates. In such a comparison, the axon would correspond to the intestine, and the Schwann cell membrane to the peritoneum. To date, no exception to this general arrangement of axon and satellite Schwann cells has been found in peripheral nerve fibers. Gasser has demonstrated, however, that in olfactory nerve fibers, more than one axon is frequently included in one of the Schwann cell invaginations. The continuity of the mesaxon has, nevertheless,

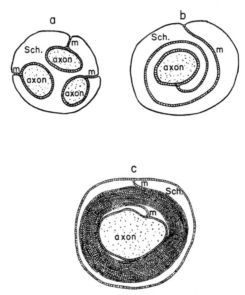

Text Fig. 3. (a) Diagram of a Schwann cell (Sch.) with three associated axons. Each axon is connected to the outside by a mesaxon (m). The gap between the apposed Schwann cell membranes and axon membranes is crosshatched. (b) Diagram of Geren's intermediate nerve fiber showing the mesaxon spirally wound about a single axon embedded in a Schwann cell (Sch.). (c) Adult myelinated fiber showing an axon embedded in a Schwann cell (Sch.) with a very greatly elongated, closely packed mesaxon wrapped many times around the axon in a spiral.

always been found. Furthermore, Gasser indicated that axons are not always completely embedded in Schwann cell troughs. Sometimes they are almost completely uncovered.

The next step in the evolution of our current conception of peripheral nerve structure came with certain observations made by Geren (29). During her studies of the formation of myelin in chick embryonic nerves, she observed certain nerve fibers consisting of a single axon surrounded by a satellite Schwann cell, in which the mesaxon was spirally elongated round the axon as indicated in Text Fig. 3b. It occurred to her that adult myelin might simply consist of a greatly elongated, and spirally wrapped, closely packed mesaxon. Shortly after this, outer and inner mesaxons were observed by Robertson (50) in adult vertebrate nerve fibers, as illustrated in Text Fig. 3c. It appeared then that Geren's postulate was correct. The implications of this conception of nerve myelin structure were of very great importance, since it was clear that if the exact relationships between the layers observed in nerve myelin and some regular, and directly related, structure of Schwann cell membranes could be established, it might be possible to apply the known information about the molecular structure of nerve myelin to the structure of cell membranes. Subsequent studies (54, 55, 62) have established such direct relationships and these will now be considered.

III. Development of Peripheral Nerve Fibers

A. *Myelinated Nerve Fibers*

During the first few days after birth, it is possible to find all stages in the development of nerve myelin in mouse sciatic nerve fibers. Plate I, Fig. 1 is a low-power survey micrograph of a 2-day-old mouse sciatic nerve in cross section. The stages in the formation of myelin which may be seen in this micrograph, have been divided arbitrarily into three groups: (1) protofibers (P); (2) intermediate fibers (I); and (3) myelinated fibers (M). *Protofibers* consist of a single axon surrounded by a satellite Schwann cell as in Text Fig. 4a (58, 60). In some instances, the axon is not completely surrounded by the Schwann cell, and in others it is completely embedded, and a mesaxon of variable length has developed. This corresponds to the earliest stage observed by Geren (29). Examples of this stage can be seen in Plate I, Fig. 1 (p), Plate II, Fig. 2 and Plate IV, Fig. 7 (p). Occasionally protofibers show closely associated cytoplasmic areas as in Plate IV, Fig. 7 (p?), and these are considered to represent fingerlike evaginations of the Schwann cell surface (60), because some of them have been traced back into the Schwann cell in serial sections. Intermediate fibers are seen in Text Fig. 4b, in Plate I, Fig. 1 (I), and in Plate III, Fig. 5. In these fibers, the

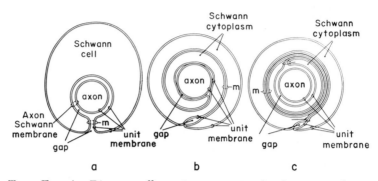

TEXT FIG. 4.   Diagrams illustrating stages in the formation of nerve myelin. In (a), a single Schwann cell envelopes a single axon. The Schwann cell and axon membrane each consist of a unit measuring about 75 A across and displaying outer dense layers bounding a light central zone. The mesaxon (m) in the young protofibers is very short. (b) Intermediate fiber showing the greatly elongated mesaxon and the closure of the gap between the unit membranes of the mesaxon and axon-Schwann membranes. (c) Young myelinated fiber showing three layers of compact myelin formed by contact of the mesaxon loops along their cytoplasmic surfaces.

mesaxon is elongated about the axon to varying degrees corresponding to the later stages observed by Geren. In some instances several mesaxon loops are observed. At a later stage, the mesaxon loops come together along their cytoplasmic surfaces

FIG. 1.   Low-power micrograph of a section of young mouse sciatic nerve. Five protofibers (p) are visible. These are characterized by a single Schwann cell with one associated axon having a mesaxon of variable length. In two of the fibers the axon is not completely enveloped by the Schwann cell, and so, no mesaxon is present. The other three show definite mesaxons in different stages of elongation into a spiral. Only one intermediate fiber (I) is seen. Here the mesaxon is elongated about the axon in more than one loop of a single spiral. A number of myelinated fibers (M) are in various stages of development. In the earliest of these, in the center of the micrograph, only three mesaxon loops have come together to form a short length of compact myelin. In the lower right-hand corner is a somewhat older myelinated fiber. Magnification: × 10,000.

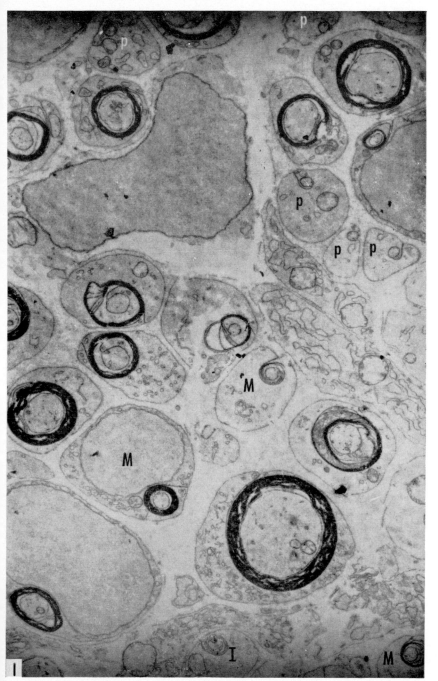

PLATE I

to make compact myelin as in Text Fig. 4c and Plate I, Fig. 1 (M).

At a higher magnification, certain important details of the organization of developing myelinated fibers may be observed. First of all, in preparations fixed with potassium permanganate (39), it is observed that the surface membrane of the Schwann cell displays a regular internal structure. It consists of a pair of dense lines measuring about 20 A across, separated by a light interzone about 35 A wide, making a unit structure about 75 A across (54, 56, 62). The exact measurements of this structure, and the contrast between the component parts are indeed very sensitive to the state of focus of the image in electron micrographs. The structure is best seen in slightly underfocused pictures as in Plate II, Fig. 4a. In micrographs closer to focus, as in Plate II, Fig. 4b, the over-all thickness of the membrane is decreased, and the contrast between the dense edges and the central zone is diminished. In overfocused images, as in Plate II, Fig. 4c, a spurious effect is found in which the structure is converted to three dense lines and two light zones. These variations in the appearance of this structure probably result from Fresnel fringe effects as well as certain phase contrast effects. Therefore, it is not possible to define with complete certainty the precise meaning of the image. The slightly underfocused image is, however, arbitrarily chosen as representative of the structure. On theoretical grounds, it can be shown that such a

FIG. 2. Section of young mouse sciatic nerve showing three stages in the evolution of protofibers. The earliest stage is at (a), and here the mesaxon is hardly formed. In (b) the mesaxon is elongated in a partial spiral about the axon. In (c), the mesaxon is further elongated. In both these fibers the gap between the unit membranes of the mesaxon is in most regions closed. Magnification: × 24,000.

FIG. 3. Adult frog myelinated nerve fiber showing an outer mesaxon (m) into which the layers of compact myelin can be traced directly. The three layers of the Schwann cell (Sch.) unit membrane are also visible at the outer surface. Magnification: × 86,000.

FIG. 4. A through-focus series of a Schwann cell surface membrane. At (a) the image is underfocused and the membrane is artificially thickened. At (b) the image is closer to focus. At (c) the image is overfocused and completely spurious. Magnification: × 320,000.

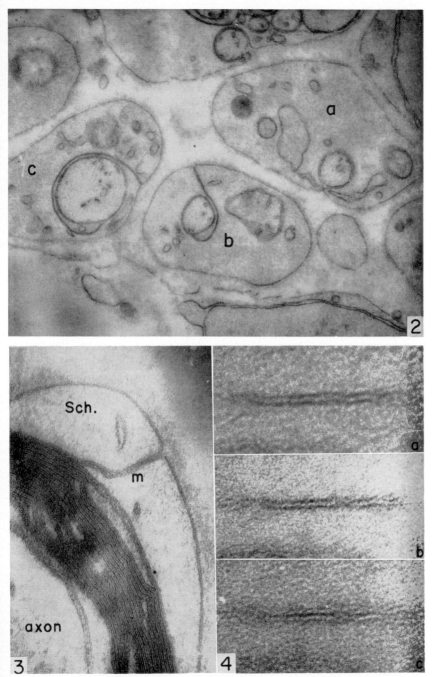

PLATE II

structure can be derived by Fresnel fringe interactions from a theoretical structure, whose component densities do not depart radically from the density distributions in the observed image. It is partly because of these electron optical uncertainties about the image, that the exact dimensions of the membrane can only be given as an approximate figure. Furthermore, there is an error of ~ 5–15% due to calibration of the magnification of the instrument used. Thus the figure ~ 75 A is only approximate at this time. This type of image, nevertheless, is consistently found in micrographs of permanganate-fixed preparations of peripheral nerve fibers as well as central nerve fibers, and at the surfaces of many other cell types. It is believed to be a true representative of cell membrane structure within the above limits.

In electron micrographs the ~ 75 A unit membrane structure can be traced directly into the mesaxons of intermediate and myelinated fibers as indicated in Plate III, Figs. 5 and 6 (55). Here the two membranes form a paired membrane structure measuring about 150 A across. In some regions, a small gap measuring ~ 50 A or less in width is present between the two unit membranes. More often, however, the membranes are found to be in contact in the mesaxons of intermediate fibers. Furthermore, the unit membranes of axon-Schwann membranes (as indicated in Plate III, Fig. 5), are also in contact in some regions. At a later stage of development, the mesaxon loops come to-

---

FIG. 5.   Transection of a portion of an intermediate fiber showing the axon surrounded by the Schwann cell (Sch.) with a mesaxon (m) elongated about the axon in almost two complete loops. Note the obliteration of the gap originally present between the unit membrane of the mesaxon and in many areas between the axon membrane and the Schwann cell membrane in the axon-Schwann membrane (ax.-Sch.). Magnification: × 130,000.

FIG. 6.   Young myelinated nerve fiber showing a Schwann cell (Sch.) and a small axon with thirteen layers of myelin. Both the outer and inner mesaxons (m) are visible. The unit membrane structure bounding the Schwann cell can also be seen (arrow u). A few components of the endoplasmic reticulum (e.r.) are present. In the inset enlargement, the junction of the outer mesaxon with compact myelin is shown. Note the formation of the major dense line (arrow) by the apposition of cytoplasmic surfaces of the mesaxon loops. The intermediate line between the major dense lines is formed by the apposed outside surfaces of the unit membranes of the mesaxon. Magnification: × 57,000. Inset magnification: × 110,000.

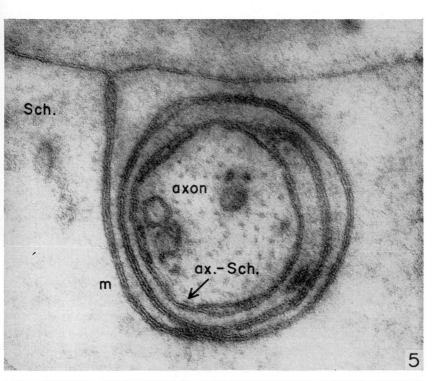

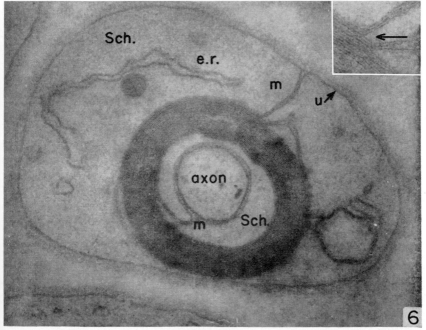

PLATE III

gether along their cytoplasmic surfaces to make compact myelin as shown in Text Fig. 4c and Plate III, Fig. 6. In Plate III, Fig. 6, thirteen mesaxon loops have come together making thirteen lamellae of myelin. These myelin lamellae are spaced at a period of about 130 A, and the dense and light zones of the unit membranes composing the original mesaxon can still be seen. The dense zones, however, have lost their distinction as separate entities, and appear instead as single, albeit thicker, fused lines. The two outside surfaces of the unit membrane make a fairly dense line bisecting each repeating lamella. The two cytoplasmic surfaces in contact make a heavier dense line (as shown by the arrow in Plate III, Fig. 6, inset). This heavy dense line is spoken of as the "major dense line" and the less dense line bisecting the lamellae as the "intermediate line."

In adult fibers these same membrane relationships are retained. In Plate II, Fig. 3 an outer mesaxon in an adult fiber is shown. Here the outermost major dense line splits as the mesaxon leaves the compact myelin structure, and the two unit membranes are reflected to form the boundaries of Schwann cytoplasm. The intermediate line also splits as the Schwann cell membranes part at the outer end of the mesaxon. Before leaving the topic of developing nerve fibers it is appropriate to present a few observations on the development of unmyelinated nerve fibers.

B. *Unmyelinated Nerve Fibers*

Plate IV, Fig. 7 and Plate V, Fig. 8 show developing unmyelinated fibers (58). Such young unmyelinated fibers in mouse sciatic nerve resemble olfactory nerve fibers in that a number of axons are included in invaginations of the Schwann cell surface [Plate IV, Fig. 7(β), Plate VI, Fig. 10(β)]. Unfortunately, it is not possible as yet to state that all of the circular contours resembling those labeled "axon" in Plate IV, Fig. 7 and Plate V, Fig. 8 are indeed axons. The density of the cytoplasm of some is higher than others, and it is likely that some of them may be evaginations of the Schwann cell surface. It is possible that some represent small growing tips of axons. The relative proportions of these remains to be determined. It is interesting and important to note that the axon and Schwann cell membrane in these fibers are frequently seen in contact with one another as indicated in Plate V, Fig. 8 (insets).

As development proceeds, the axons grouped together in single invaginations of the Schwann cell surface, as in Plate IV, Fig. 7(β), or assembled about multiple extensions of Schwann cells, as in Plate IV, Fig. 7(α) and Plate V, Fig. 8, appear to separate, and tend to occupy single troughs of their own, as in Plate IV, Fig. 7(γ) and Plate VI, Fig. 10(β). Plate VI, Fig. 10 includes unmyelinated fibers in a 16-day-old mouse sciatic nerve. As development advances, the axon and Schwann cell membranes, which are in contact at the early stages, separate from one another, and a gap of 100–150 A in width appears between the membranes as in the dotted area of Plate VI, Fig. 10 enlarged in Plate VI, Fig. 11. This appearance is more characteristic of adult unmyelinated fibers. At this stage the unit membranes of axons and Schwann cells are characteristically separated by wider gaps, and are very rarely seen in contact with one another.

Heretofore, only micrographs of nerve fibers fixed in potassium permanganate have been considered. We may now examine fibers fixed in another way, since this may aid in an evaluation of the degree to which the permanganate picture is true of the original structure.

IV. Comparison of OsO_4- and $KMnO_4$-Fixed Fibers

Plate VII, Fig. 12 is a micrograph of an adult myelinated fiber fixed in OsO_4 (58). Note that the general picture of the myelin is similar, in that lamellae repeating at a period of about 120 A are seen. Furthermore, the outer and inner mesaxons (m) are clearly visible. In one region the intraperiod line can be faintly discerned, although in other places it is not clear. Note that the major dense line originates (arrow) by the apposition of the *cytoplasmic* surfaces of the mesaxon loops in the same way that it originates in permanganate-fixed preparations.

This relationship is of crucial importance, for the dense layer next to the cytoplasm originating at the major dense line can be traced directly to the Schwann cell surface, where its continuity is retained. Here it measures as little as 20 A, but is quite variable in width and appearance. The intraperiod line in this outermost layer of myelin near the arrows, however, is not clearly visible. Furthermore, as the unit membranes of the mesaxon separate at the surface of the Schwann cell, the outside layer of the unit membrane is not seen. It is clear, nevertheless, that this outside layer of the unit membranes composing myelin has reality, even though it cannot be seen at the free surfaces of the Schwann cell. This follows from two facts. First, the intraperiod line does appear in some regions in the compact myelin structure. Second, even where it is not seen, the spacing between the major dense lines is the same. Interestingly, there are a few spots at the free surfaces of such Schwann cells in which a faint suggestion of the outer dense component of the unit membrane can be seen. It thus appears probable that the outer dense part of the unit membrane structure after OsO_4 fixation has been lost during the remaining preparatory procedures. Despite its loss at the free surfaces of the Schwann cell in OsO_4-fixed preparations, its presence is nevertheless still manifested in the compact myelin structure itself by the regularity of the periodic lamellae. Permanganate fixation not only shows the same regularity in the myelin lamellae, but preserves the structures responsible for the spacing even at

FIG. 7. Twelve protofibers (p) in various stages of development in a section of young mouse sciatic nerve. Also, several developing unmyelinated fibers (α, β, and γ) are visible. These can be divided into three groups. In group (α), a number of axons and very much smaller structures resembling axons are partially or completely surrounded by several Schwann cells (Sch.). Some of the round profiles among the presumed axons are very small (order of several hundred angstrom units). Some of these may represent growing tips of young axons or minute fingerlike processes of the Schwann cell. Another type of developing unmyelinated fiber is seen at (β). Here groups of axons and small round profiles appear to be associated with single Schwann cells. Some of these fibers of type (β) are aggregated into bundles with their associated Schwann cells in contact (upper right). One such fiber is enlarged in Plate V, Fig. 8. Still another type of unmyelinated fiber is represented at (γ). In this case a single large Schwann cell is seen invaginated by three separate axons (ax.). In this case the endoplasmic reticulum of the Schwann cell is very abundant. Magnification: × 6,000.

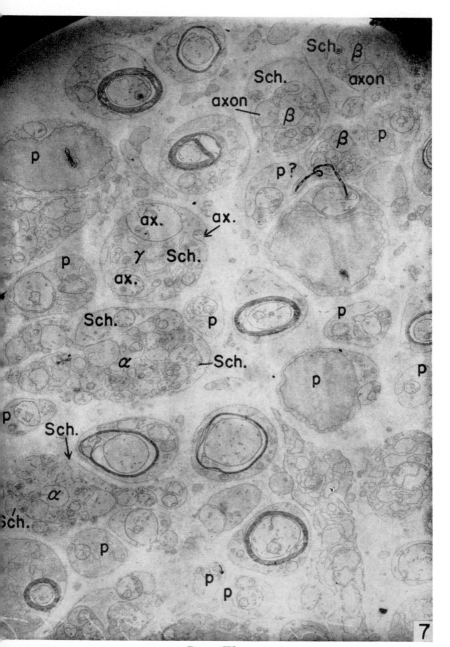

PLATE IV

the free surfaces of the Schwann cells (Plate II, Fig. 3). It seems, therefore, that permanganate fixation gives a more correct and reliable representation of the cell membrane structure than OsO_4 fixation.

Plate VII, Fig. 13 compares in more detail myelin in OsO_4 with myelin fixed in $KMnO_4$. In Plate VII, Fig. 13a after fixation in OsO_4 the major dense lines are prominent and the intraperiod lines appear as irregular lines or granules. This is the type of structure originally observed in myelin by Sjöstrand (77) and Fernandez-Moran (17). The spacing of the periodic structure is between 100 and 120 A. In Plate VII, Fig. 13b the same kind of structure after permanganate fixation again shows distinct major dense lines repeating at a period of about 120 A but the intraperiod lines are much more regular and distinct. The latter appear less dense than the major dense lines if the time of fixation does not exceed 4 hours. In Plate VII, Fig. 13c the effect of more prolonged fixation in potassium permanganate is shown. Here the density of the intraperiod line has increased until it approximately equals that of the major dense line. This is a consistent finding and occurs

FIG. 8.   High-power micrograph of a developing unmyelinated fiber, like the type (β) in Plate IV, Fig. 7. Here a number of round profiles are seen surrounded by cytoplasmic areas presumed to represent Schwann cells (Sch.). The larger of these round profiles seem to represent axons. However, the smaller ones are difficult to label. Some may represent growing tips of young axons or fingerlike evaginations of Schwann cells. The axon-Schwann membrane gaps in some regions are closed as indicated by the enlarged dotted areas in the insets. Magnification: $\times$ 23,000; Inset magnification: $\times$ 130,000.

FIG. 9.   Longitudinal section of a portion of a Schmidt-Lantermann cleft. Note that each myelin lamella traverses the cleft intact after splitting away from the myelin sheath along the major dense lines as indicated in the lower right inset. Note the circular profiles seen in the cytoplasmic regions between the lamellae traversing the cleft. One of these is enlarged in the upper right inset to show the unit membrane bounding it. The outer Schwann surface membrane with a caveola appears to the right, and the axon-Schwann membrane to the left of the myelin. Note the gap between the unit membranes of the axon-Schwann membrane in this region. Magnification: $\times$ 60,000; upper inset magnification: $\times$ 180,000; lower inset magnification: $\times$ 140,000.

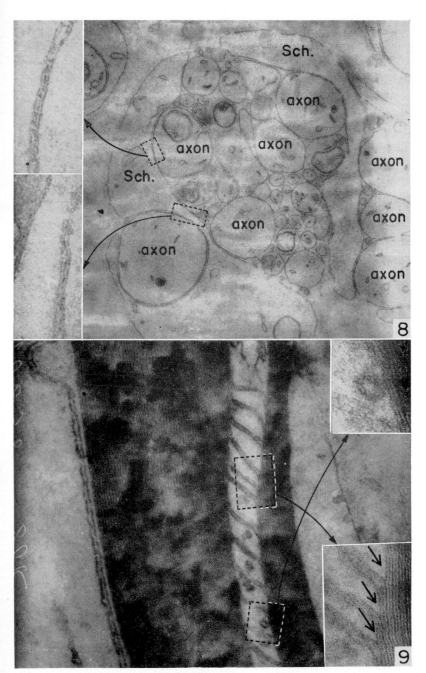

Sch.

axon

axon

axon

axon

axon

Sch.

axon

axon

axon

axon

8

9

PLATE V

after more than 6 hours' fixation with permanganate (*18, 54, 62*). The period here is effectively reduced to ~ 60 A, and this kind of periodic structure probably corresponds to the layered structure observed by Fernandez-Moran in OsO_4-fixed frozen sections when he obtained the first electron micrographs of the myelin period (*16*). These findings all lead to the important conclusion that the outside surface of the Schwann cell membrane differs chemically from the inside surface.

V. POLARIZATION OPTICAL AND X-RAY DIFFRACTION STUDIES OF NERVE MYELIN

W. J. Schmidt studied the properties of nerve myelin in polarized light (*68*). He found that the optic axis of the myelin sheath is radially directed, and that the sheath is strongly birefringent with the slow axis of transmission of its index ellipse radially directed. He deduced that this radial positivity was due to radially oriented smectic layers of lipid molecules. Furthermore, he suggested that these layers of lipid might alternate with tangentially ordered layers of protein. Subsequent studies by Chinn and Schmitt (*5a*) and Schmitt and Bear (*71*) confirmed Schmidt's observations on the optical properties of myelin, and also led to the conclusion that the positive radial birefringence was due to layers of radially oriented lipid molecules. Chinn and Schmitt extracted the lipid component with lipid solvents, and observed a reversal of the sign of the radial birefringence to negativity. They fixed the resulting altered nerve

---

FIG. 10.   Section of a 16-day-old mouse sciatic nerve. Developing unmyelinated fibers of the types (β) and (γ) seen in Plate IV, Fig. 7 are present.   In (β), a bundle of round profiles, presumably representing axons. is surrounded by a single Schwann cell. At (γ), a larger Schwann cell (Sch.) area is seen with a number of associated axons and round profiles of lesser diameter which are difficult to identify. Some of the apparent axons in this case occupy single troughs of their own. At this stage of development it is rare to see a closure of the gaps between unit membranes. This is made clear by the enlarged dotted square shown in Fig. 11. Magnification: × 15,000.

FIG. 11.   Dotted area indicated in Plate VI, Fig. 10. Note the gaps between the unit membranes of the axon and Schwann cell (Sch.) and the small unidentified processes (pr.). Magnification: × 200,000.

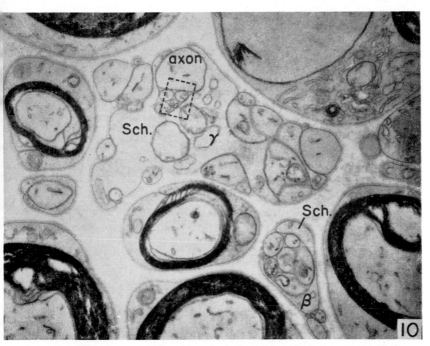

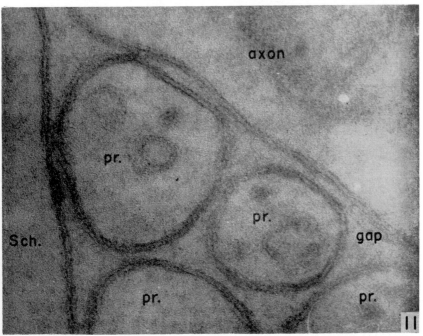

PLATE VI

fibers with a chemical fixative and prepared histological sections of the fibers on which form birefringence studies could be conducted. They found that the radial negativity after lipid extraction was due to form birefringence, and deduced that this was due to tangentially oriented layers of protein molecules identifiable with the so-called neurokeratin. It thus appeared reasonable to suppose that myelin consisted of alternating layers of tangentially disposed protein molecules with radially disposed layers of lipid molecules between them.

During this same period, Schmitt, Bear, and Clark (72) and subsequently, Schmitt, Bear, and Palmer (73), studied the nerve myelin sheath by small-angle X-ray diffraction techniques. They found a radial repeat period of about 170 A in frog nerve fibers and about 180 A in mammalian nerve fibers. They obtained alcohol-ether extracts from nerve fibers, which were found to form organized systems when mixed with water. These lipid model systems also gave small-angle X-ray diffraction patterns with a fundamental repeat period of 66 A. They obtained further patterns from purified lipid fractions known to be present in nerve, and found several spacings varying from ~ 40–60 A. These agreed closely with the calculated spacing to be expected from bimolecular leaflets of the lipids under study. They found, furthermore, that by increasing the water content the spacing of the crude alcohol-ether extracted nerve lipids could be made to increase 100%. They interpreted these findings as indicating that such lipid systems organize themselves into bimolecular leaflets, with the nonpolar carbon chains of the lipid molecules

FIG. 12. Portion of an adult frog myelinated nerve fiber fixed with OsO_4. The outer and inner mesaxons (m) are shown. The intraperiod line cannot be seen clearly. Fairly thick layers of Schwann cytoplasm (Sch.) are visible both outside and inside the myelin layers. Note the origin of the major dense line by the apposition of the cytoplasmic surfaces of mesaxon loops (arrow). The outer Schwann cell surface membrane below does not show the unit membrane structure which is characteristically seen after permanganate fixation (see Plate II, Fig. 3). Magnification: × 100,000.

FIG. 13. Myelin fixed in OsO_4 (a) is compared with myelin fixed with $KMnO_4$ for a short time (b) and a long time (c). Magnification: × 700,000.

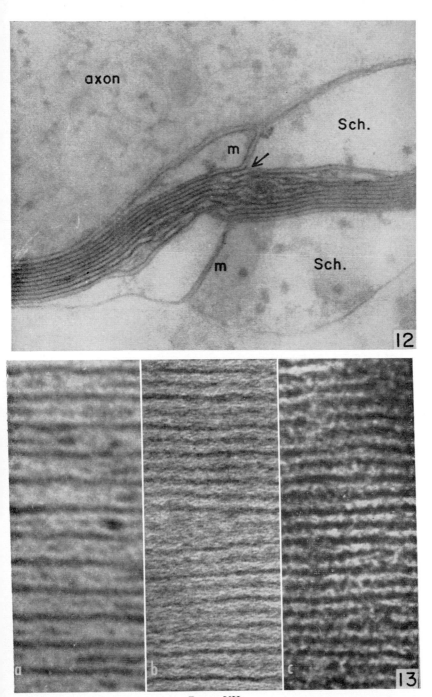

PLATE VII

oriented toward the central regions of the leaflets and the polar surfaces toward the aqueous layers. On the basis of these findings, they postulated a number of different possible configurations of lipids and proteins that might correspond to the radial repeat unit found in myelin. The lipid molecules were assumed to be arranged radially, because of the intrinsic birefringence of the myelin of fresh fibers, and the protein molecules tangentially, because of the form birefringence findings. The four most probable configurations postulated are presented in Text Fig. 5.

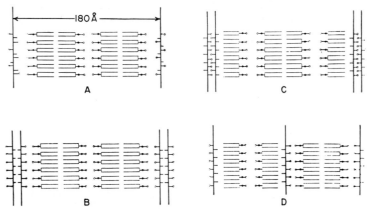

TEXT FIG. 5.   Myelin sheath structures (radial direction). Four possible patterns of organization of the lipid and protein molecules in the repeating unit in nerve myelin taken from Schmitt, Bear, and Palmer (72).

Subsequently, Elkes and Finean (12–14) and Finean (19, 21) have studied myelin by X-ray diffraction techniques, and have arrived at a general conception similar to that of Schmitt, Bear, and Palmer, but differing in certain details. Finean's latest conception of the radial repeat unit in myelin is presented in Text Fig. 6 (21). It will be seen in this diagram that he considers it probable that each myelin repeat unit contains two bimolecular leaflets of mixed lipids, the polar surfaces of which are covered by monolayers of nonlipid material. This structure is symmetrical and if the nonlipid components were all identical, the period would be half that observed. Finean was able, by slight modifications of peripheral nerve, to bring about a halving of the period. He also observed that, under certain conditions, optic nerve myelin exhibits a half period. For these reasons, he believes that the nonlipid layers occurring at the half period position differ only slightly from those at the boundaries of the repeat unit. He refers to this factor bisecting the unit cell of the periodic structure as the "difference factor" (21, 22). The component responsible for the "difference factor" differs only slightly in X-ray

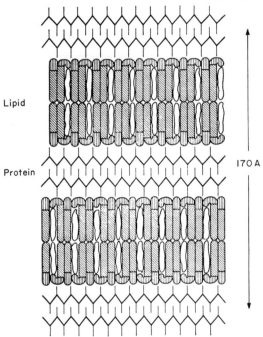

Lipid

Protein

170 A

TEXT FIG. 6.   Finean's conception of the molecular organization of the 170 A repeat unit in nerve myelin (21).

scattering power from that bounding the unit cell, but it cannot be said that it and the other layers are necessarily protein. It seems probable that some of the layers are protein, but the X-ray data do not exclude the possibility that one set of the nonlipid layers may be something else—perhaps carbohydrate.

Finean (20) and Fernandez-Moran and Finean (18) have studied the changes occurring in peripheral nerve myelin during fixation and embedding in methacrylate, preparatory to the observation of nerve fibers in thin sections by electron microscopy. They found that the 170–180 A period is immediately reduced to less than 120 A after fixation with OsO_4. The period increases somewhat during the dehydration procedures with lipid solvents. It continues to increase to about 140–150 A during embedding in methacrylate. After the preparation of sections of methacrylate-embedded OsO_4-fixed fibers a periodic repeat structure measuring about 120 A is consistently seen. As a thin section of methacrylate-embedded tissue is subjected to the electron beam in an electron microscope preparatory to taking a micrograph, a great deal of shrinkage occurs. The magnitude of the shrinkage is difficult to measure, but it is sufficient to account for the decrease in the period from 140–150 A down to the observed values in electron micrographs (51). Very little variation in the period occurs in correlation with the direction of sectioning, and a similar shrinkage artifact is evident, though to a lesser extent, in Araldite-embedded tissues.

It is clear from the previous discussion that the repeating unit in myelin is the mesaxon or surface-connecting membrane. Taking into account preparatory artifacts, this repeating unit corresponds almost exactly to the expected repeat period detected by X-ray analysis of living fibers. Therefore, it seems reasonable to conclude that the X-ray repeat unit contains two unit membranes each of which is simply a Schwann cell membrane enfolded and packed back-to-back. Thus we can superimpose the molecular structure of the X-ray repeating unit as produced by Finean on the repeating unit as observed by electron microscopy, and extrapolate to the Schwann cell surface as in Text Fig. 7 (24, 62). It is possible on this basis to conclude that the ~ 75 A unit membrane seen at the Schwann cell surface probably contains a single bimolecular leaflet of lipid, the polar surfaces of which are covered by monolayers of nonlipid material. Furthermore, the alternation of inside and outside layers readily explains the difference factor of Finean. It should be emphasized that the molecular structure deduced for the unit membrane on this basis depends for its accuracy on the exactness of the X-ray analysis.

There is nothing in the electron microscope observations which could lead directly to the conclusion that the unit membrane has the molecular structure postulated. However, if the conclusions arrived at by the X-ray diffraction studies are correct, then the Schwann cell membrane probably has the general pattern of structure illustrated in Text Fig. 8.

VI. Studies of Model Systems

In their early X-ray diffraction studies of nerve myelin structure, Schmitt and his co-workers carried out certain studies of

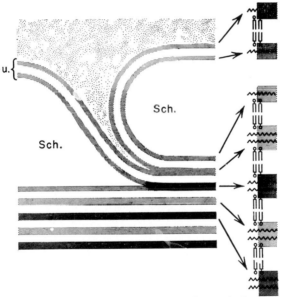

Text Fig. 7.   To the left three myelin lamellae with the outer mesaxon are shown. The unit membrane structure (u.) bounding the Schwann cell (Sch.) is shown. The relatively heavy major dense lines are formed by the apposition of the cytoplasmic surfaces of the unit membranes of the mesaxon. The mesaxon, on symmetry grounds alone, is the repeating unit of nerve myelin. To the right, the molecular repeat unit deduced from X-ray diffraction data is shown. Only two myelin lamellae are included in the molecular diagram. It is possible to extrapolate from this molecular diagram directly to the Schwann cell surface, and to conclude that the Schwann cell surface membrane probably has the molecular structure indicated to the upper right. This conclusion depends for its accuracy largely on the accuracy of the X-ray analysis.

model lipid systems that are of importance in understanding the molecular structure of myelin. These have been discussed above.

In an effort to extend such studies by means of electron microscopy, the author has carried out similar extractions of nerve tissue (59). The following experimental procedure was adopted.

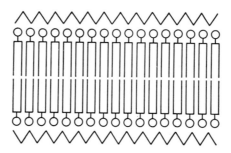

TEXT FIG. 8. Diagram of the probable molecular pattern of the unit membrane structure as deduced from a combination of X-ray diffraction data with evidence derived from electron microscopy. Phospholipid molecules are indicated very schematically by the tuning fork structure with their polar groups shown as circles. The zig-zag lines are intended to represent nonlipid monolayers.

Several whole cat brains, spinal cords, and peripheral nerves were placed, immediately after dissection, into a large volume of 50:50 alcohol:ether at about 4°C. The container was sealed and kept at about 4°C for a period of several months. A flocculent, fairly abundant, white crystalline precipitate soon appeared in the container. Upon examination in polarized light this precipitate was found to be composed of strongly birefringent crystals, occurring primarily as long, thin, rectangular plates. These displayed negative birefringence with respect to the long axis of the plates. This crystalline material was dried and labeled fraction H (Plate VIII, Fig. 14). The supernatant alcohol-ether solution was then filtered with a sintered glass filter and slowly dried in an evaporating dish at room temperature. A light brownish waxy noncrystalline material was obtained and labeled fraction W. When examined in polarized light this appeared amorphous. Each of these fractions was studied further as follows.

Plate VIII, Fig. 14 is a light micrograph of one of the crystals of fraction H in polarized light with a $\lambda/30$ Köhler compensator arranged so that the crystals appear light on a dark background because of their negative birefringence. Upon immersing these crystals in distilled water, they immediately dissolved. Upon drying, new, somewhat longer and thinner, but similar negatively birefringent crystals reappeared. A sample of this material was placed in each of two test tubes and covered with cold $KMnO_4$ and OsO_4 fixative, respectively. In each case, the sign of the birefringence of the crystals immediately reversed. The material did not dissolve completely in either tube, and the resulting sediment was dehydrated and embedded in Araldite for sectioning.

Plate VIII, Fig. 15 is an electron micrograph of a section of crystals of fraction H fixed with $KMnO_4$. Irregularly disposed parallel sheets of dense material are observed. The material is thickened laterally in irregularly distributed plaque-like areas. At higher magnification, these plaque-like regions of thickening display a regular, layered structure, consisting of dense lines less than 20 A across, repeating radially at a spacing of about 40 A (Plate VIII, Fig. 16). The plaques taper down to a limiting structure consisting of a single pair of dense lines each $\sim$ 20 A wide making a unit (Plate VIII, Fig. 17) resembling somewhat the unit membrane structure seen at the surfaces of cells, but measuring here only about 50 A across.

The same essential procedure with similar results was carried out on the material of fraction H fixed in OsO_4. However, in this case, the tapering layered plaque-like structures seemed somewhat larger, and the parallel unit arrangement observed in Plate VIII, Fig. 17 was not so prominent. A high-power micrograph of one of the tapering tactoid-like layered structures after OsO_4 fixation is shown in Plate VIII, Fig. 18.

The waxy fraction W, upon being covered with distilled water, showed no immediate change such as that shown by fraction H. However, within a period of a few minutes, distinct myelin forms began to appear at the edges of the material. One of these is shown in Plate VIII, Fig. 19. In this light micrograph one myelin form is shown between crossed polaroids with a Köhler compensator so arranged that the structure appears light against a dark background because of its negative birefringence with respect to its long axis. Upon replacing the water about the myelin forms with $KMnO_4$ fixative, the motion of the forms ceased immediately, but the sign of the birefringence remained the same. Upon immersing the material in OsO_4 fixative, a similar cessation of motion was apparent immediately, but there was also an immediate reversal of the sign of birefringence. Samples of fraction W were fixed in $KMnO_4$ and OsO_4 and embedded for sectioning for electron microscopy. In each case, layered structures repeating at a period of ∼ 40 A were observed, but the periodic structure was much more frequently

---

FIG. 14. Crystals of fraction H in polarized light with a Köhler compensator so arranged that the crystals appear bright on a dark background, because of their negative birefringence with respect to the long axis.

FIG. 15. Low-power micrograph of crystals of fraction H fixed with permanganate, embedded in Araldite, and sectioned. Magnification: × 8,500.

FIG. 16. A plaque-like area resembling that seen in Fig. 15 (arrow) at a very much higher magnification. Notice the dense layers less than 20 A wide repeating at a period of about 40 A. Magnification: × 200,000.

FIG. 17. The tapering end of one of the plaque-like thickenings like those seen in Figs. 15 and 16, also after permanganate fixation. Here the plaque has tapered down to a single unit consisting of a paired dense line making a unit measuring about 50 A across. Magnification: × 180,000.

FIG. 18. One of the plaque-like regions, like those seen in Figs. 15 and 16 after fixation of the crystals of fraction H. Fixation in this case however, was with OsO_4 rather than permanganate. Magnification: × 150,000.

FIG. 19. A myelin form which arose from the waxy fraction W after soaking for a few minutes in water. It is seen in polarized light with a compensator arranged so that the structure appears bright on a dark background because of its negative intrinsic birefringence with respect to the long axis. Note the change in the sign of birefringence at the ends of the form. Magnification: × 250.

FIG. 20. Section of a sample of the waxy fraction W fixed with potassium permanganate, embedded in Araldite, and sectioned. The material was not soaked in water before fixation and the observed structure cannot be considered as a myelin form. Note the irregularly disposed layers under 20 A in thickness repeating at a period of about 40 A. Magnification: × 120,000.

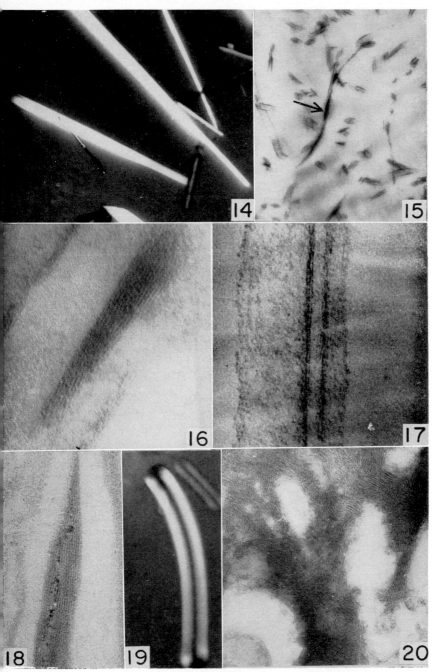

PLATE VIII

found and more clearly seen in the KMnO₄-fixed material (Plate VIII, Fig. 20).

While these studies were in progress, Ito and Revel (35) reported preliminary findings on studies of myelin forms produced from a phospholipid fraction of egg yolk. They fixed these with OsO₄ and in some cases observed unit layers which consisted of single dense lines measuring somewhat under 100 A in thickness. After further study, Ito and Fawcett (34) found that the previously observed single dense lines were in fact paired lines, making a unit less than 100 A thick. Each dense line made up about one third of the thickness of the unit, and there was a zone of lesser density between the bounding layers.

These studies could be interpreted in several ways, but any final interpretation must await detailed chemical analysis of the constituents responsible for the densities observed by electron microscopy. The fraction H component obtained from cat nerve might be partly protein. Fraction W, because of its waxy character and the ready organization of myelin forms is probably largely lipid. However, the degree to which each fraction is contaminated with other material has not yet been determined. It is of great interest, however, to find that both fraction H and the lipid fraction of Ito and Fawcett display, in sections of regions including the smallest number of layers, a limiting membrane-like structure consisting of two dense lines bounding a light center instead of a single dense line. In both materials, the observed structures greatly resemble the unit membrane seen at the surfaces of cells.

It is important now to determine precisely how the observed densities are produced. It is necessary to decide whether or not they represent primarily protein or lipid components, and if the latter is concerned to what extent the densities represent one or the other end of the lipid molecules. Undoubtedly, these densities reflect, to a great extent, a deposition of osmium and manganese, but it is by no means clear whether or not the deposited metals reside at sites of reaction with specific groups within the molecular species concerned. They may have migrated to other sites. In fact, the original reacting molecules may no longer be present in recognizable form after fixation. Furthermore, it is necessary to analyze in greater detail the degree to which Fresnel fringe effects in the electron microscope images are contributory to the density distributions observed. Much further work is required, but it is clear that this type of study has great bearing upon the problem of the molecular structure of nerve myelin and of cell membranes generally.

During the course of the above studies, Stoeckenius (79, 80) conducted similar electron microscope studies of a lipid fraction obtained from human brain. His results have not yet been published in full and hence will not be considered in detail here. However, Dr. Stoeckenius has kindly given permission for certain of his results to be discussed briefly. In essence, he obtained a lipid fraction from brain which he was able to purify and characterize chemically, so that he feels confident that the fraction consists of pure mixed lipids. This material did not fix well with $KMnO_4$, but after OsO_4 fixation, layered structures similar to those reported here were observed repeating at a period of about 40 A. Stoeckenius performed certain experiments in which he was able to deposit before fixation very thin layers of protein on the surface of some of the layered aggregates in his preparations. He has shown that the layered regions are apparently unaltered by the protein deposition, and he saw an irregular amorphous material of lesser density appearing at the boundary of the layered regions, which is presumed to be the protein component. He found that this amorphous protein "material" fused with the outermost dense layer of the layered structure. He also observed single units in the protein-treated material measuring about 100 A across, consisting of two dense lines separated by a very narrow central light zone. His interpretation of these findings is as follows: (1) The dense lines measuring less than 20 A observed in the layered structure, represent osmium deposited along the nonpolar carbon chains of phospholipid molecules, at sites of reaction with double bonds. (2) The light region between the dense lines is a region occupied by the polar groups of the phospholipid layers. (3) Protein interacts with the outermost layer of phospholipid molecules so that the nonpolar ends of the lipid molecules are curled around to form associations with relatively nonpolar side chains of the protein. As a result of these interpretations, Stoeckenius believes that the structure measuring less than 100 A and resembling the unit membrane in his material, consists of two bimolecular leaflets of lipid bordered on either side by very thin layers of protein. If there is any correlation, other than a coincidental one, between this observed model structure and the observed cell membrane structure in nerve fibers, it might be necessary to suppose that the correct molecular model of the unit membrane structure as observed in cells, contains twice as much lipid as hitherto believed. If such were the case, it would be necessary to postulate four bimolecular leaflets of lipid instead of two for each repeating unit in nerve myelin. It is not yet decided with certainty, but it seems improbable, that the X-ray data can be reasonably reinterpreted in this way. Nevertheless, these observations and interpretations by Stoeckenius have focused attention on the possibility that the conclusions deduced by X-ray diffraction with respect to the molecular structure of myelin need reexamination.

Certain observations recently reported by Mercer (43) bear on the above problems. He was able to prepare fairly thick films of lipid and of protein on water surfaces, and to fix these with OsO_4 and embed and section them for electron microscopy. He found dense layers several hundred angstroms thick displaying no internal structure. It is of great interest, however, that the density of the fairly thick sheets of both lipid and protein in the sections after fixation are about equal. His findings indicate that the density produced by the reaction of lipids and of proteins with OsO_4 are about equal. This disposes of any notion of differentiating lipids from proteins in layered structures such as myelin on the basis of density differences alone.

VII. GAP SUBSTANCE

In permanganate-fixed tissues of many different types, the boundaries between closely associated adjacent cells appear characteristically as paired membrane structures. Each membrane of the pair displays the typical unit membrane structure and measures about 75 A across (56, 61–63). The two unit membranes are separated by a gap measuring usually about 100–150 A across. A paired membrane structure of this type is shown in Plate IX, Fig. 21. This is the type of membrane relationship that is found in adult unmyelinated nerve fibers generally (Text Fig. 9). During development, as indicated above, the gap between the unit membranes is often closed in such nerve fibers, but closures of this type are not often seen in adult unmyelinated fibers. It was found possible, however, to produce closures of the gaps between the membranes of unmyelinated fibers by soaking the nerves in hypertonic Ringer solution before fixation (57, 60). At concentrations of twice normal or more, such closures are a prominent feature of sections of unmyelinated fibers. Examples are shown in Plate IX, Fig. 22 and Plate X, Figs. 23 and 24 (see Text Fig. 10). In Plate IX, Fig. 22 axon-Schwann membranes, inter-Schwann cell membranes, and mesaxons are seen with their unit membranes in contact. In Plate X, Figs. 23 and 24, the entire mesaxons of unmyelinated fibers display the phenomenon of gap closure. The over-all width of the intercellular boundary is reduced from its normal value of 250 to 300 A to about 150 A and the two outer ∼ 75 A unit membranes are in very close contact. In Plate X, Fig. 23, hypertonicity was brought about by increasing the concentration of Ringer solution in which the fibers were bathed prior to fixation to 4 × the normal value. In Plate X, Fig. 24 sucrose was dissolved in normal Ringer solution so as to increase the total molarity to 10 × the normal value. In Plate IX, Fig. 22 the entire Schwann cell is surrounded by a moderately dense amorphous material (g) which extends into the gaps between the cell membranes of mesaxons. This material is sometimes observed concentrated in a dense layer near the outer surface of the membranes at the free edges of the cell, and after OsO_4 fixation and heavy staining with phosphotungstic acid, this region appears as a membrane-like structure sometimes referred to by the term "basement membrane." This hazy material seen at the surface of Schwann cells extends, in some cases, for indefinite distances into the intercellular space largely occupied by collagen fibrils.

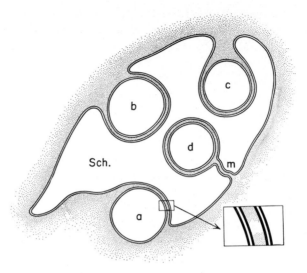

Text Fig. 9.   Diagram of an adult unmyelinated nerve fiber showing a single Schwann cell (Sch.) with four associated axons (a, b, c, and d). The Schwann cell and axon membranes each consist of a pair of dense lines about 20 A across separated by a light zone about 35 A wide making a unit of about 75 A in thickness. These are indicated in the diagram. The axons are embedded to varying degrees in the Schwann cell. Axon (d) is completely enveloped, and the two lips of cytoplasm extend around it to make a paired membrane structure called the mesaxon (m) or surface-connecting membrane.

Fig. 21.   Section of the boundary between two smooth muscle cells in mouse intestine. Cytoplasm of each of two muscle cells is located above and below. Each cell is bounded by a unit membrane structure (u). The unit membranes are separated by a gap of about 100 A in this case. Magnification: × 500,000.

Fig. 22.   Portion of an adult frog unmyelinated nerve fiber soaked in hypertonic Ringer solution before fixation with permanganate. One axon is seen with a mesaxon (m). The Schwann cell (Sch.) around this axon is in contact with, and partially surrounded by, another Schwann cell. Note the amorphous appearing material (g) surrounding the surface of the fibers. The inset enlargements show the unit membrane structures in contact with one another in the dotted areas. Magnification: × 100,000; Inset magnification: × 150,000.

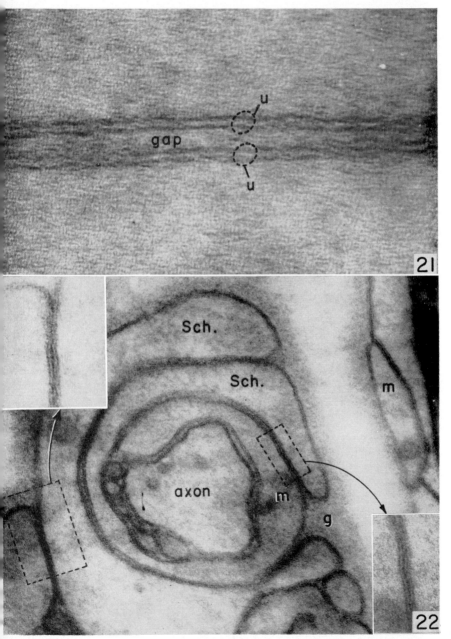

PLATE IX

It is probably representative of the intercellular ground substance. This substance probably extends into the gaps between
paired membrane structures, such as mesaxons, and axon-
Schwann membranes. After treatment with hypertonic solutions,

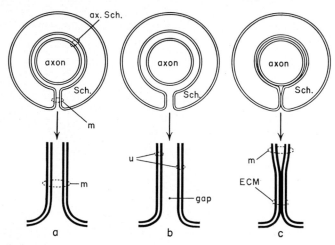

TEXT FIG. 10.   Diagrams depicting the effect of hypotonic and hypertonic
Ringer solutions on the membrane relationships of unmyelinated nerve
fibers. Such fibers are represented schematically by single axons surrounded
by single Schwann cells (Sch.). The unit membrane (u) of the axon
Schwann membrane (ax. Sch.), and the mesaxon (m) are spaced about
100–150 A apart normally, as indicated in (a). After soaking in hypotonic
solutions, these gaps are widened as indicated in (b); and after soaking in
hypertonic solutions, the gaps are reduced as indicated in (c). Sometimes
the gaps are completely closed, and the two unit membranes come together
along their outside surfaces as indicated in (c) to make a compound membrane structure, referred to as an external compound membrane (ECM).

it seems as if this intercellular substance collapses as the paired
membranes come into very close contact with one another.

One way of interpreting these closures of the gaps of mesaxons,
is to consider the gap substance to be a very highly hydrated,
mucopolysaccharide gel. The collapse of the gap could then be
interpreted as a syneresis phenomenon. An alternative interpretation could be made if the gap substance is ignored, and it
is postulated that charged groups on surfaces of the adjacent

paired membranes are responsible for the positions they assume with respect to one another. Hypertonic Ringer solution might then bring about an alteration in these charged groups, which could lead to a change in the positions of the membranes, and might result in a more intimate contact as observed in the micrographs. However, the effect obtained with sucrose alone could hardly be interpreted in exactly the same way.

In an effort to resolve this particular problem, an experiment has recently been performed in this laboratory with washed red blood cells. Red blood cells display the ~ 75 A unit membrane structure in permanganate-fixed material (56, 62, 64). When intimately associated with one another (presumably in rouleau formation), red cells are separated in normal preparations by a gap in every way like that seen between cells in normal tissues. If the gap substance is not involved in the alterations of the membranes observed in hypertonic solutions, then it should be possible to bring about a more intimate contact of red cell membranes by immersing thoroughly washed red cells in hypertonic solutions. Preliminary experiments in this direction have failed to show a collapse of the intermembranous gaps between washed red cells. The width of the gaps is approximately the same in washed red cells that have been treated by twice normal and ten times normal saline. This preliminary finding supports the conception that the phenomenon observed in nerve fibers is more attributable to a collapse of the gap substance, than an alteration of charges present at the surfaces of the membranes alone.

Other experiments of this type have been conducted on nerve fibers, and these bear on the binding forces between membranes in nerve myelin. Finean and Millington (23) have shown that an increase in the myelin period occurs if myelinated nerve fibers are soaked in hypotonic solutions. This increase in the period has been studied by electron microscopy, and is found to be due to separation of the membranes in myelin along the intraperiod line (57, 60, 63). In other words, the gap originally present in the embryonic mesaxon reopens in hypotonic solutions, so that the myelin period is greatly increased. It is very interesting to observe, however, that even after soaking in distilled water the membranes do not separate along the cytoplasmic surfaces of the unit membrane united embryonically at the major dense line. This is illustrated in Plate X, Fig. 25 and in Text Fig. 11. This finding suggests that the binding forces holding the myelin membranes together are of two kinds. One kind appears to operate between the closely associated outside cell surfaces, and is affected by treatment with hypotonic solutions. The other kind operates between closely associated cytoplasmic surfaces, and is not affected by hypotonic solutions.

The type of paired membrane association illustrated in Plate IX, Fig. 21 was stated to be characteristic of intercellular boundaries in all tissues. This is correct in so far as information is now available, but there are certain exceptions to this rule in nerve fibers, and it appears that these exceptions may be of significance with regard to nerve impulse propagation, since they occur in such structures as nodes of Ranvier and Schmidt-Lantermann clefts. We shall turn now to a brief consideration of the structural arrangements observed at these two vital parts of peripheral nerve fibers.

FIG. 23.   Portion of an adult unmyelinated fiber soaked in Ringer solution of four times the isotonic concentration before fixation with permanganate. Note the complete closure of the mesaxon (m) of the Schwann cell (Sch.) leading to the axon. This mesaxon is enlarged to the left to show the unit membrane structures. Magnification: × 90,000; Inset magnification: × 500,000.

FIG. 24.   Portion of another unmyelinated fiber similar to that shown in Fig. 23, but in this case soaked in Ringer solution made hypertonic by the addition of sucrose to ten times the isotonic molarity. The enlarged view of the mesaxon to the left shows details of the unit membrane structures. Magnification: × 68,000; Inset magnification: × 400,000.

FIG. 25.   Portion of a myelinated nerve fiber soaked in distilled water before fixation with permanganate. The nucleus (nuc.) of the Schwann cell (Sch.) appears to the left. The outer and inner mesaxons of the myelin are visible, and a segment of myelin including the inner mesaxon is enlarged to the left to show the separation of the myelin lamellae along the intraperiod lines. Magnification: × 30,000; Inset magnification: × 50,000.

FIG. 26.   Transection of a small myelinated fiber near a node of Ranvier. Note the endoplasmic reticulum components in the axon and the thin myelin sheath. The outer mesaxon (m) is visible but the inner mesaxon is not seen. Magnification: × 22,000.

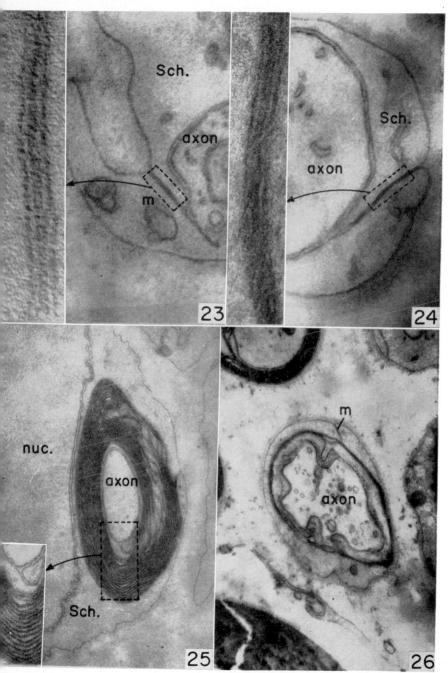

PLATE X

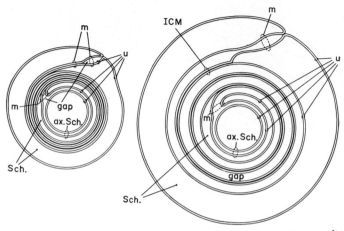

TEXT FIG. 11.   Diagram illustrating the effect of immersing myelinated fibers in water before fixation. The Schwann cell (Sch.) increases in over-all diameter. The intraperiod lines split and the myelin lamellae separate from one another restoring the primitive mesaxon gap. The lamellae do not separate along the cytoplasmic surfaces of the mesaxon loops united em-bryonically at the major dense line. The mesaxons (m) are visible before and after treatment. The unit membranes (u) are unaltered. The axon-Schwann membrane (ax. Sch.) is not greatly altered. The paired membrane structure, measuring about 150 A across, consisting of two unit membranes united along their cytoplasmic surfaces left in the myelin sheath, is referred to by the term internal compound membrane (ICM).

VIII.   SPECIAL STRUCTURES OF PERIPHERAL NERVE FIBERS

A.   *Nodes of Ranvier*

Vertebrate myelinated nerve fibers are completely enclosed by the myelin sheath described above, except at the nodes of Ranvier. Nodes occur at intervals of a few hundred microns up to several millimeters in most myelinated fibers. Here the myelin sheath is completely absent over a very short length of the axon. Several reports dealing with electron microscope studies of nodes have now appeared (*15, 24, 26, 40–42, 52, 53, 63a, 81*). It is now possible to describe with some precision the membrane arrangements at these regions.

A characteristic feature of nodes of large fibers, known since the earliest light microscope descriptions, is a relative narrowing of the axon near the termination of the myelin sheath (Plate XI, Fig. 27) (32). The axon may be reduced by about one third of its total diameter in this region. Some believe that this narrowing is partly an artifact occurring during fixation (85). This matter is difficult to assess, but the narrowing is a constant feature of nodes of large fibers seen in electron micrographs, and the complexity and regularity of the structural features observed is such, that it seems improbable that the relative narrowing is entirely produced during fixation. However, the degree of artifact remains an open question.

Plate XI, Fig. 27 is a micrograph of a longitudinal section through a node in a medium-sized fiber. In such sections, it can be seen that each lamella of the myelin sheath separates as a mesaxon from the axonal side of the compact myelin structure, as the node is approached. These mesaxons are spaced a few tenths of a micron apart, and Schwann cytoplasm is identifiable in the intervening separations. The planes of these mesaxons lie roughly perpendicular to the fiber axis in the juxtaterminal myelin region, and they are, therefore, only seen clearly in longitudinal sections. As the myelin becomes very thin and terminates, the planes of the mesaxons tilt gradually, until the last few are directed nearly parallel to the long axis of the fiber (Plate XI, Figs. 27 and 28). Over most of the juxtaterminal myelinated region, the outer mesaxon is invisible in longitudinal section. In cross sections of this region, however, the outer mesaxon is clearly apparent, and the inner mesaxons cannot be seen (Plate X, Fig. 26). These findings are best interpreted by the assumption that only one continuous membrane structure is concerned. This continuous structure in compact myelin is a myelin lamella, and within the compact myelin it is cut perpendicularly, either in longitudinal or transverse sections. Outside compact myelin, it is a mesaxon. The apparent multiplicity of mesaxons seen at nodes, results from the way in which this single structure is oriented, so that it is cut almost perpendicularly many times in any longitudinal section, but only once perpendicularly in any cross section. The difference between longitudinal and transverse sections results from a change of orientation of the plane of the mesaxon as it comes to lie external to the juxtaterminal myelin. Here the mesaxon plane rotates about an axis perpendicular to the fiber axis, until its plane eventually includes the latter, i.e., it runs roughly parallel to the fiber axis.

This arrangement of the myelin lamellae in the terminal region at nodes can easily be understood in terms of the spiral myelin conception as indicated in the diagrams of Text Fig. 12. A plasticine model was constructed when these structures were first observed (52). A cylindrical piece was taken to represent the axon. The myelin sheath was represented by a thin sheet of plasticine cut in the shape indicated in the diagram (a). When this sheet was rolled around the cylinder representing the axon (b), the edge of the sheet directed toward the node was found to inscribe a helix on the surface of the cylinder. After the sheet was completely wound around the cylinder, a longitudinal section was cut (c–e). The edges of the sheet, wound helically around the axon, appeared in a disposition similar to that seen

FIG. 27. Longitudinal section of a node fixed in permanganate. Note the constriction of the axon occurring in the juxtaterminal myelinated region and the slight bulge of the axon in the unmyelinated region of the node. The unmyelinated nodal region is characterized by a collar of minute processes (pr.) of the two Schwann cells meeting at the node. The nodal axon frequently contains bodies measuring a few tenths of a micron in diameter surrounded by a single unit membrane, and containing numerous round profiles bounded by unit membranes (mu). Axon filaments are visible running longitudinally through the nodal region and components of the endoplasmic reticulum (e.r.) are frequently seen. Magnification: × 16,000.

FIG. 28. Longitudinal section through a small myelinated fiber including a node of Ranvier. Note the features of similarity with the node shown in Plate XI, Fig. 27. However, the relative constriction of the axon at the nodal region is not noticeable. Note the relatively great extent of the unmyelinated part of the node surrounded by a very thin layer of nodal processes. Magnification: × 7,500.

FIG. 29. Segment of the juxtaterminal myelinated region near a node showing the manner in which mesaxons peel off the myelin sheath by a separation of the unit membranes united at the major dense line. Note that the outside surfaces of the unit membranes united at the intraperiod line remain in contact in the mesaxon. As the unit membranes come into contact with the axon membrane (arrow), the outer surface of the axon membrane and of the Schwann cell unit membranes are also in contact. Magnification: × 48,000.

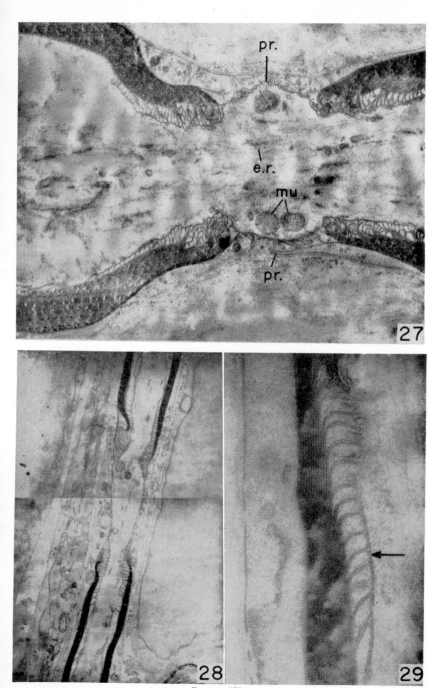

PLATE XI

in nerve fibers if the edges were considered to represent the mesaxons (24, 52, 53, 55).

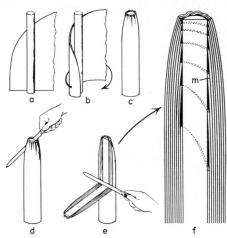

Text Fig. 12.   Stages in the construction of a model to represent the myelin sheath at nodes of Ranvier. See the text for explanation of a–e. In (f) the section of the nodal region cut away in (e) is shown at higher magnification. Note the mesaxons (m) appearing in the longitudinal section.

In the juxtaterminal myelinated region of the node, the Schwann cell membrane and the axon membrane are in intimate contact with one another (55) (Plate XI, Fig. 29; Text Fig. 13). The gap, which is usually present between unit membranes in this type of structure, has not been seen in such regions in per-manganate-fixed preparations. The gap by contrast is usually present in the axon-Schwann membrane in the internodal regions of the fiber.

The nodal axon completely free of myelin bulges slightly (Plate XI, Figs. 27 and 28), and extends for a variable distance, which is related to fiber diameter. Typically, the unmyelinated nodal axon extends for about 0.5 μ in larger (10–15 μ) fibers. In small (3–10 μ) fibers on the other hand, the nodal axon ex-tends for as much as 2.5 μ along the length of the fiber (Plate XI, Fig. 28). The nodal axon is not entirely uncovered. It is sur-rounded by a collar of minute fingerlike processes of the two

Schwann cells (*24, 53*). These fingerlike processes measure about 500 A in diameter and are of undetermined length. They are tangled about the nodal axon in a very irregular fashion, so that in any section, either longitudinal or transverse to the fiber axis, some processes may be seen cut either transversely or longitudi-

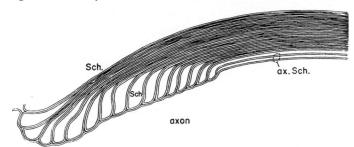

TEXT FIG. 13. Diagram showing the relationships between the unit membranes of myelin, and the axon in the juxtaterminal myelinated regions of nodes. The axon as shown below and Schwann cytoplasm is indicated by (Sch.). The axon-Schwann membrane (ax. Sch.) appears to the right. Note that there is a definite gap between the Schwann cell membrane and the axon membrane in this region. As the mesaxons peel off the axonal side of the myelin sheath, the Schwann cell and axon membranes are in intimate contact throughout the juxtaterminal myelinated region. The gap is effectively obliterated in this region (see Plate XI, Fig. 29).

nally. These nodal Schwann cell processes are shown in a longitudinal section in Plate XI, Fig. 27, and in transverse sections in Plate XII, Figs. 30 and 31. Occasionally only one layer of these processes is seen forming the collar around the axon, and in such cases transverse sections show them as in Plate XII, Fig. 31. Here most of the processes are cut transversely, and therefore run roughly parallel to the fiber axis. The unit membrane structure can be clearly observed bounding these nodal processes, although cytoplasmic organelles are not visible in the smaller terminal ones. The axonal membrane in the nodal region again displays the unit membrane structure, but in some areas the membrane is folded, so that the layers of the unit membrane cannot be seen clearly. The kind of membrane contact relationships observed in the juxtaterminal myelinated region are not apparent here (see Plate XI, Fig. 29 and Text Figs. 13 and 14). The axon membrane and the Schwann cell membrane bounding the nodal processes are not in contact with one another. Instead, there is a

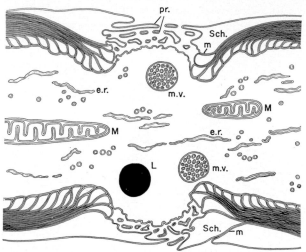

TEXT FIG. 14. Diagram summarizing the various structures observed at nodes. The nodal axoplasm contains moderately abundant tubular components of the endoplasmic reticulum (e.r.), mitochondria (M), multivesicular bodies (m.v.), and large, very dense, presumably lipid bodies (L). The nodal axoplasm bulges slightly at the node. The juxtaterminal myelin region is as described in Text Fig. 13. Sometimes, however, the mesaxons (m) are somewhat complicated in appearance by the retraction of some of the terminal rings of Schwann cytoplasm (Sch.), as indicated to the lower right. The axon-Schwann membrane gap is closed over the juxtaterminal myelinated region. At the unmyelinated nodal region the gaps are present and measure about 100–150 A across. This region is covered by numerous fingerlike processes (pr.) extended by the two Schwann cells meeting at the node.

FIG. 30. Cross section of a node of Ranvier showing the collar of irregular nodal processes (pr.) cut in various orientations around the axon. Tubular components of the endoplasmic reticulum (e.r.) and mitochondria (M) are seen in the nodal axon. The mitochondrion shown here is closely related to the axon surface. Magnification: × 60,000.

FIG. 31. Transection of a node in a very small fiber surrounded by a layer of nodal processes (pr.). One of these processes with the associated axon membrane is enlarged in the upper right inset. Note the 100–250 A gap between the unit membranes of the axon and the nodal process. Magnification: × 60,000; Inset magnification: × 100,000.

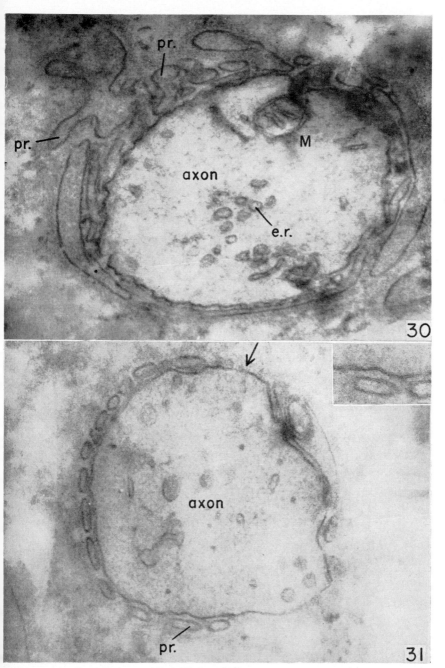

PLATE XII

gap of rather variable width between them. A similar gap occurs between the membranes of adjacent Schwann cell processes in the nodal collar. It is clearly important to know the dimensions of these gaps, but it is difficult to state very precise figures. In the juxtaterminal myelinated region, the gap between the axon and Schwann cell membranes is so small that it usually is not resolved (i.e., it is probably less than 20 A). It is comparable to the gaps present between the unit membranes within compact myelin. Over the unmyelinated part of the node the gaps measure anywhere from $\sim$ 100 to $\sim$ 250 A (see Plate XII, Fig. 31). It is important to realize however, that in no case in this region have the membranes so far been observed in contact with one another. Some of the variations in the gap widths measured here are real (Plate XII, Fig. 31, inset) while others probably are exaggerated by oblique sectioning. Occasionally, a relatively large expanse of nodal axon may appear completely exposed to the outside (Plate XII, Fig. 31, arrow). This may be more apparent than real, since the section might include the plane of the gap between two adjacent nodal processes, and only part of each process, so that their membranes are so oblique as to be invisible in the section. Data are being accumulated now, and it is hoped that fairly accurate estimates of exposed nodal membrane area can be given in the near future. These different membrane contact relationships at nodes result in a relative restriction of the axon-Schwann membrane gap in the juxtaterminal myelin region, as compared with the unmyelinated nodal region. If the gap is considered a possible pathway for ionic current flow between axoplasm and the outside during action potential propagation, this restriction may be important.

The thickness of the collar of nodal processes around the axon is also of interest. In very large fibers (10–15 μ) in which the length of the unmyelinated nodal axon is relatively short ($\sim$ 0.5 μ), the thickness of the collar of nodal processes is relatively great. It may measure as much as 1 μ radially. Typically in small fibers, in which the extent of the unmyelinated nodal axon may be as much as 2.5 μ, the radial extent of the collar of nodal processes is very much smaller (Text Fig. 15). In such cases only

one layer of processes may be present as indicated in Plate XI,
Fig. 28 and Plate XII, Fig. 31.

This arrangement at nodes, whereby a relatively larger proportion of axon membrane in small fibers is directly exposed to the
outside, than in larger fibers, may be connected with the fact that

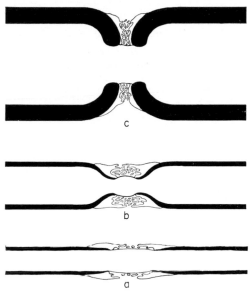

TEXT FIG. 15.   Diagram illustrating the arrangement of the collar of
nodal processes of Schwann cells about nodes of Ranvier in fibers of different sizes. In the smallest fibers the collar is relatively thin as in (a) and
(b) but it is spread over a relatively greater length. In larger fibers, the
thickness of the collar is much greater, but its extent along the axon is
reduced (c).

small fibers have a higher threshold for electrical stimulation than
larger fibers. This difference in threshold is understandable partly
on the basis of size alone, since the larger fibers would be expected to carry a larger proportion of any stimulating currents
running longitudinally between two electrodes placed along the
fiber axis. This factor alone might be sufficient to explain differences in threshold. It is a striking fact, however, that in many
large fibers the exposed area of nodal axon membrane is actually

smaller than in many small fibers. Thus the current density at the nodal membrane is probably much higher in large fibers than in small fibers. This also may be an important factor in explaining the differences in threshold to electrical stimulation between large and small fibers and one wonders if it may not be related to velocity of conduction as well.

All these findings concerning double membrane gaps may be very significant in connection with the mechanism of propagation of nerve impulses, since it is possible that the gaps between the unit membranes in paired membrane structures, like mesaxons and axon-Schwann membranes, may be pathways for ionic current flow between the axon surface and the outside during impulse propagation (25, 49, 70). In fact, one might say that the membrane contact relationships at nodes could provide a morphological basis in myelinated fibers for saltatory conduction. The only other potentially important pathway for current flow might be the Schmidt-Lantermann clefts. Therefore, the structure of these interruptions in the myelin sheath will now be considered.

B. *Schmidt-Lantermann Incisures*

Schmidt-Lantermann incisures or clefts are funnel-shaped discontinuities in the myelin sheath, sometimes occurring at intervals of a few microns. These interruptions have been observed repeatedly by light microscopists since their first description by Schmidt (67) and by Lantermann (37) over seventy-five years ago. Much speculation has been presented regarding their nature, and many have considered them to represent artifacts. However, Lantermann observed the incisures clearly in fresh, unfixed, and minimally damaged nerve fibers and did not consider them to represent artifacts. Subsequent workers, including Nageotte (46) and Ségall (76) and many others (86) have repeatedly described these structures. It is true that any observation of the clefts in living fibers may be associated with damage, and so it is still contended by some that the clefts result from damage to the myelin. It is said that the more a nerve fiber is manipulated, the more closely spaced and numerous are the clefts. This controversy can hardly be settled by electron microscopy alone. The structure of the clefts, however, has now been fairly well defined by electron microscopy (59), and there are certain facts which support the view that the clefts are not entirely artifactitious (27); though the matter is by no means settled.

Gasser (26) presented the first electron microscope observations on the Schmidt-Lantermann incisures. In his preparations, it appeared that the incisures might in fact represent complete discontinuities of myelin, and hence a wide open pathway for current flow. However, it soon became apparent that such was not the case. Luxoro (40, 41) studied the structure of Schmidt-Lantermann incisures and observed membranes transversing the clefts, which might be expected to interfere with any free flow of constituents through the myelin. A similar conclusion was reached by Uzman and Nogueira-Graf (81) and by the author (59). A longitudinal section of a portion of a Schmidt-Lantermann incisure is shown in Plate V, Fig. 9. It is evident that the myelin lamellae traverse the cleft intact, and that the interruption in the sheath is due to separation of the lamellae by a splitting of the major dense line (see arrows in Plate V, Fig. 9). This means that the cytoplasmic surfaces of the mesaxon loops united during development at the major dense line separate from one another (see Text Fig. 16). In addition, there is a slight separation of the two outside surfaces of the unit membrane as the cleft is traversed. However, this separation, which restores the original mesaxon gap, is not very wide, and rarely exceeds 50 A. In some cases, no separation is seen. The lamellae traversing the cleft are relatively widely separated (order of 0.1 μ). Sections of the outermost lamellae traversing the cleft show clearly that this interlamellar space is connected directly with the outer layer of Schwann cytoplasm. Similarly the inner layer is connected with the very thin layer of Schwann cytoplasm which lies between the innermost myelin lamella and the axon-Schwann membrane. Circular profiles a few hundred angstroms in diameter, and bounded by unit membranes, are seen occasionally in these interlamellar regions within Schmidt-Lantermann clefts (Plate V, Fig. 9—upper inset). It appears probable therefore, that the interlamellar separations are associated with an entrance of cytoplasm into the myelin sheath.

A number of variants in the organization of these interruptions of myelin have been observed. Sometimes the direction of the incisure in longitudinal section is reversed, so that the structure appears V-shaped as originally described by Ségall (*76*). This has been observed in electron micrographs. Sometimes the cleft is

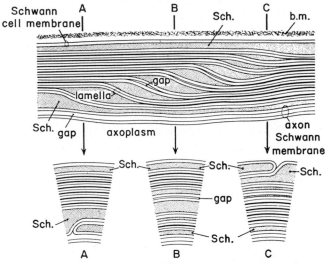

TEXT FIG. 16. Diagram of a Schmidt-Lantermann cleft. Above, the cleft is shown in longitudinal section. Schwann cytoplasm (Sch.) is stippled. The basement membrane layer (b.m.) is shown separated somewhat from the Schwann cell membrane. Below at (A), (B), and (C) the appearance of the cleft in transverse section is indicated. Actually the lamellae traversing the cleft in (B) probably would not be seen in electron micrographs because of their obliquity in the section.

FIG. 32. Transverse section of a classical Schmidt-Lantermann cleft. Note that the lamellae traversing the cleft are not visible. This is due to their obliquity in the section. The outer and inner mesaxons (m) in Schwann cytoplasm (Sch.) are visible. Magnification: × 15,000.

FIG. 33. Transverse shearing defect of the Schmidt-Lantermann type observed in a 16-day-old mouse sciatic nerve. Here the lamellae traversing the cleft are clearly visible in transverse section. Compare with Fig. 32 and Text Figs. 16 and 17. Note the circular profile observed between the outermost lamellae and the next one in the shearing defect. Magnification: × 40,000.

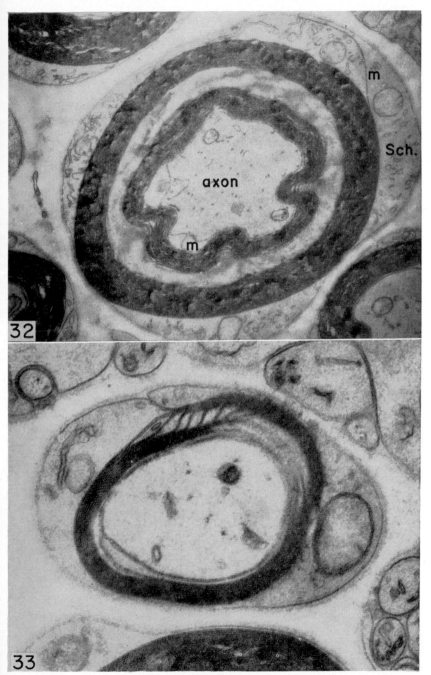

PLATE XIII

not complete. It may extend only partly through the myelin, or may appear on only one side of the fiber. This suggests that the clefts may be undergoing dynamic changes during fixation.

In transverse section, certain similar types of shearing discontinuity have been found by electron microscopy. Plate XIII, Fig. 32 presents the usual appearance of a cross section of a classic Schmidt-Lantermann cleft. It will be observed, that the membranous structures traversing the cleft cannot generally be seen in this transverse section. This is due to the obliquity with which they pass through the plane of the section. Quite frequently in electron micrographs, discontinuities resembling Schmidt-Lantermann clefts are seen in transverse sections. These shearing defects are also produced by the splitting apart of the lamellae along the major dense lines. Presumably the interlamellar space is occupied by Schwann cytoplasm, though direct connections between this space and Schwann cytoplasm have not been established. Indeed, from longitudinal sections it appears that these separations represent isolated pockets. The outside surfaces of the unit membranes of the lamellae in these transverse separations remain closely associated as in Schmidt-Lantermann incisures. A transverse shearing defect of this type may be observed in Plate XIII, Fig. 33. A defect of this type could easily be derived from a typical Schmidt-Lantermann incisure if most of the shearing separations of the lamellae were obliterated. A few remaining pockets could then be rearranged along the longitudinal axis of the fiber to yield a composite defect which would appear in transverse sections. No matter what their exact origin may be, these transverse shearing defects are a consistent feature of myelinated fibers at all stages of development. Text Fig. 17 presents a diagram of one of the transverse shearing defects.

It does not seem unreasonable to suppose that the Schmidt-Lantermann incisures develop in response to mechanical stresses and strains introduced by normal postural changes in peripheral nerve fibers; and that as they develop, Schwann cytoplasm enters the myelin sheath, and communicates with the very thin layer of cytoplasm next to the axon. This flow of cytoplasm might serve the function of providing occasional, more direct, connections between the inner layer of Schwann cytoplasm and the outer nucleated layer, as well as bringing the Schwann cell membrane, relatively isolated in compact myelin, occasionally into contact with Schwann cytoplasm. This might serve a function in terms of metabolic turnover in the membranes themselves. The struc-

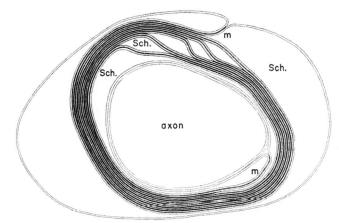

TEXT FIG. 17. Diagram of a transverse shearing defect in myelin resembling a Schmidt-Lantermann cleft. The axon is surrounded by a Schwann cell (Sch.) which has formed six lamellae of myelin. The lamellae traverse the cleft intact, united along their outside surfaces, and separated by layers of Schwann cytoplasm as in the classical Schmidt-Lantermann cleft. The outer and inner mesaxons (m) are shown. Compare with Plate XIII, Fig. 33.

tural arrangement is such that a long helical pathway from the axon-Schwann membrane gap through the incisures to the outside is provided, but this pathway is extremely long and very thin. Furthermore, it is sometimes interrupted. It seems probable therefore, that such a pathway would carry relatively little ionic current as compared with the pathways available at nodes. Nevertheless, the incisures may be important in this connection.

IX. A GENERAL MOLECULAR THEORY OF CELL MEMBRANE STRUCTURE

It is interesting to know whether or not the type of membrane structure observed at the surfaces of Schwann cells is of general occurrence. It has been shown above, that it is possible to make certain deductions about the molecular structure of the Schwann cell unit membrane because of its importance in myelin formation. But what of other cells? Is such a unit structure present everywhere, and, if so, can any generalization be made about the molecular structure of membranes?

A number of tissues have been examined by electron microscopy using the preparation techniques utilized in the study of nerve fibers. It has been found in every case, that cells of widely divergent types in vertebrates and invertebrates, are bounded by a unit membrane structure which appears in every respect the same as that which bounds Schwann cells and axons (56, 62). The tissues surveyed in particular animals include the following: *frog:* skin, intestinal epithelium, liver, pancreas, muscle, nerve, red blood cells, connective tissue cells, and endothelial cells; *cat:* liver, kidney, and skeletal muscle; *mouse:* nerve, skeletal muscle, smooth muscle, intestinal epithelium, liver, kidney, fibroblasts, endothelial cells, and eosinophils; *crayfish:* nerve; *crab:* muscle; *human:* red and white blood cells (64).

Others working in this laboratory have found the same type of structure in chick embryonic cells [Bellairs (1)], locust nerve tissue [Gray (31)], and mouse cornea [Whitear (84)]. The ~ 75 A unit membrane structure is seen most clearly and consistently after $KMnO_4$ fixation but it has also been seen after OsO_4 fixation. Essentially the same type of unit has been reported by others in several other types of tissue fixed either with OsO_4 or $KMnO_4$, although interpretations have differed. These include hair follicle cells [Birbeck and Mercer (4)], tissue culture cells and amoebae [Mercer (44)], grasshopper spermatids and protozoan ciliates [Roth (65, 66)], and mouse intestinal mucosa [Sjöstrand and Zetterqvist (78) and Zetterqvist (87)]. The same type of unit membrane measuring about 75–100 A in thickness has been observed in plant tissues after OsO_4 fixation by Buvat and Lance (5).

Roth (66) and Sjöstrand and Zetterqvist (78) gave figures of 100 A for the over-all width of the unit membrane structures in their preparations. These figures probably should not be considered significantly different from the ~ 75 A figure given here, because methods of calibration and measurement as well as slight fixation and focusing differences might account for the discrepancy. Slight differences have been observed in the way in which the layers of the unit membrane structure appear in certain regions after permanganate fixation. Thus, the outer dense layer at the striated border of intestinal epithelial cells appears somewhat hazy and less sharply defined, although the boundary of the same cells deeper in the epithelium, appears the same as in other cells. The same sort of fuzziness of the outer dense layer is seen in the brush border of the kidney. A micrograph of intestinal epithelial cells is shown in Plate XIV, Fig. 34. To the upper right an inset enlargement shows the membrane of the microvillae. Note the sharpness of the cytoplasmic border and the fuzziness of the outer boundary. Nevertheless, the over-all thickness of the membrane is not far from ~ 75 A; though the outer limit is rather arbitrary, and measurements of over 100 A might be made. The intercellular boundary between two cells of this epithelium away from the luminal border is shown in the inset to the upper left. Note that here the appearance of the unit membrane is the same as seen elsewhere. An additional point of interest is the contact of the unit membranes near the luminal boundary of the intercellular paired membrane.

Plate XIV, Fig. 35 presents a portion of a renal glomerulus showing the unit membrane structure on a podocyte (P) and the endothelial cells (E). The endothelial cells are broken up into many small interdigitating processes. The difference seen at the outer boundary of proximal convoluted tubular cells and the striated border in the intestine, are perhaps related to the absorption of material during the period in which the fixative acted, since no effort to control these processes was made. It is interesting, in this connection, that after OsO_4 fixation, Sjöstrand and Zetterqvist (78) saw both the outer and inner dense layers of the unit membranes as symmetrical structures in mouse intestine if fixation was carried out after a period of starvation. They were not able to see the layers of the structure clearly if fixation was carried out immediately after feeding. Thus, it seems reasonable to conclude that the same essential pattern of molecular structure may underlie the membranes observed at absorptive surfaces as those seen elsewhere.

In every instance in which clear preparations have so far been obtained after permanganate fixation and Araldite embedding, it has been possible to demonstrate the unit membrane structure in membranous cell organelles including mitochondria (56, 60, 62), endoplasmic reticulum (62), Golgi membranes, and so-called synaptic "vesicles." An example of the unit membrane structure seen in endoplasmic reticulum in a Schwann cell is given in Plate XIV, Fig. 36.

The above findings lead to the general conclusion that the unit membrane structure is probably universally present in all animal, and possibly all plant, cells. Furthermore, it seems probable that the pattern of structure seen in permanganate-fixed preparations represents a central core of a bimolecular leaflet of lipid, bounded on either side by monolayers of nonlipid material. The conclu-

---

FIG. 34. Section of a portion of the luminal border of mouse small intestinal epithelial cells. The microvilli are slightly obliquely sectioned. A small group is enlarged in the right upper inset to show the characteristics of the membrane structure. A portion of the intercellular paired membranes near the luminal border in the dotted square is enlarged to the upper left to show the unit membrane structure. In this region the unit membranes are in contact toward the luminal border. Note the zone near the microvilli in which the cells are relatively free of the abundant endoplasmic reticulum which characterizes them throughout other regions. Magnification: × 23,000; Right inset magnification: × 46,000; Left inset magnification: × 130,000.

FIG. 35. Section through a part of a renal glomerulus in mouse kidney. The podocytes (P) appear to the right along the basement membrane (b.m.) which lies between them and the endothelium (E) bounding the capilliary (Cap.) lumen. The endothelial cells appear to be broken up into numerous microvillous projections, which interdigitate along the basement membrane boundary, leaving gaps in between, permitting free axis to the capillary lumen. The peculiar mitochondria-like body in the large podocyte process near the lower center region is not understood. Magnification: × 65,000.

FIG. 36. A saclike component of the endoplasmic reticulum of Schwann cytoplasm in a peripheral myelinated nerve fiber. Note the characteristic unit membrane structure (u) bounding the sac. The membrane measures about 75 A across. Magnification: × 320,000.

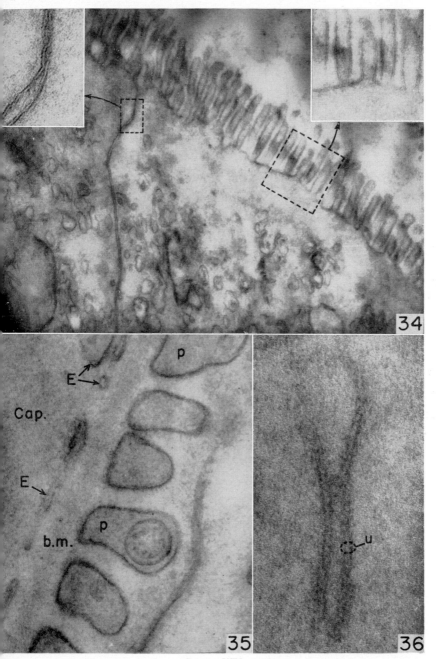

PLATE XIV

sion about molecular structure is based almost entirely on X-ray diffraction evidence. The morphological observations stand on their own and give new scope and meaning to the X-ray data, but cannot as yet lead directly to conclusions about the molecular structure. If the X-ray data should be reinterpreted in some other way, the interpretation of the unit membrane structure in molecular terms would have to be altered accordingly. On present evidence, however, the interpretation given seems reasonable. A structure such as this could include many different kinds of lipid compounds as well as many different kinds of nonlipid material. It is the over-all pattern of organization which is considered to be constant in all cells.

REFERENCES

1. Bellairs, R. *J. Embryol. Exptl. Morphol.* **6**, 149-151 (1958).
2. Bernhard, W. *Nature* **170**, 359-360 (1952).
3. Bessis, M., and Bricka, M. *Rév. hématol.* **5**, 396-427 (1950).
4. Birbeck, M. S. E., and Mercer, E. H. *J. Biophys. Biochem. Cytol.* **3**, 223-230 (1957).
5. Buvat, R., and Lance, A. *Compt. rend.* 1-3 (1957).
5a. Chinn, P., and Schmitt, F. O. *J. Cellular Comp. Physiol.* **9**, 289-296 (1937).
6. Cole, K. S. *J. Cellular Comp. Physiol.* **1**, 1-9 (1932).
7. Cole, K. S., and Cole, R. H. *J. Gen. Physiol.* **19**, 609-623 (1936).
8. Cole, K. S., and Cole, R. H. *J. Gen. Physiol.* **19**, 625-632 (1936).
9. Danielli, J. F., and Davson, H. *J. Cellular Comp. Physiol.* **5**, 495-508 (1935).
10. Danielli, J. F., and Harvey, E. N. *J. Cellular Comp. Physiol.* **5**, 483-494 (1935).
11. Davson, H., and Danielli, J. F. "The Permeability of Natural Membranes." Cambridge Univ. Press, London and New York, 1943.
12. Elkes, J., and Finean, J. B. *Discussions Faraday Soc.* **6**, 134-143. (1949).
13. Elkes, J., and Finean, J. B. *Exptl. Cell Research* **4**, 69-81 (1953).
14. Elkes, J., and Finean, J. B. *Exptl. Cell Research* **4**, 82-95 (1953).
15. Engstrom, H., and Wersall, J. *Exptl. Cell Research* **14**, 414-425 (1958).
16. Fernandez-Moran, H. *Exptl. Cell Research* **1**, 309-337 (1950).
17. Fernandez-Moran, H. *Progr. in Biophys. and Biophys. Chem.* **4**, 112-147 (1954).
18. Fernandez-Moran, H., and Finean, J. B. *J. Biophys. Biochem. Cytol.* **3**, 725-748 (1957).

19. Finean, J. B. *Exptl. Cell Research* **5**, 202-215 (1953).
20. Finean, J. B. *Exptl. Cell Research* **6**, 283-293 (1954).
21. Finean, J. B. *In* "Biochemical Problems of Lipids," pp. 127-131. Butterworths, London, 1956.
22. Finean, J. B. *Exptl. Cell Research, Suppl.* **5**, 18-32 (1958).
23. Finean, J. B., and Millington, P. F. *J. Biophys. Biochem. Cytol.* **3**, 89-94 (1957).
24. Finean, J. B., and Robertson, J. D. *Brit. Med. Bull.* **14**, 267-273 (1958).
25. Frankenhaeuser, B., and Hodgkin, A. *J. Physiol.* **131**, 341-376 (1956).
26. Gasser, H. S. *Cold Spring Harbor Symposia Quant. Biol.* **17**, 32-36 (1952).
27. Gasser, H. *J. Gen. Physiol.* **38**, 709-728 (1955).
28. Gasser, H. *J. Gen. Physiol.* **39**, 473-496 (1956).
29. Geren, B. B. *Exptl. Cell Research* **7**, 558-562 (1954).
30. Gorter, E., and Grendel, R. *J. Exptl. Med.* **41**, 439-443 (1925).
31. Gray, E. G. *Phil. Trans. Roy. Soc. London Ser.* In press.
32. Hess, A., and Young, J. B. *Proc. Roy. Soc.* **B140**, 301-391 (1952).
33. Hillier, J., and Hoffman, J. F. *J. Cellular Comp. Physiol.* **42**, 203-247 (1953).
34. Ito, S., and Fawcett, D. W. *J. Biophys. Biochem. Cytol.* **4**, 135-142 (1958).
35. Ito, S., and Revel, J. P. *Anat. Record* **130**, 319 (1958).
36. Langmuir, I. *J. Am. Chem. Soc.* **37**, 1848-1905 (1917).
37. Lantermann, A. J. *Arch. mikroskop. Anat. u. Entwicklungsmech.* **13**, 1-8 (1877).
38. Latta, H. *Blood* **7**, 508-521 (1952).
39. Luft, J. H. *J. Biophys. Biochem. Cytol.* **2**, 799-801 (1956).
40. Luxoro, M. Ph.D. Thesis, Massachusetts Institute of Technology, Cambridge, Massachusetts, 1956.
41. Luxoro, M. *Proc. Natl. Acad. Sci. U.S.* **44**, 152-156 (1958).
42. McAlear, J. H., Millburn, N. S., and Chapman, G. B. *J. Ultrastructure Research* **2**, 171-176 (1958).
43. Mercer, E. H. *Proc. Intern. Conf. Electron Microscopy, 4th Conf., Berlin*, p. 204 (1958).
44. Mercer, E. H. *Proc. Roy. Soc.* **B150**, 216-232 (1959).
45. Mitchison, J. M. *Symposia Soc. Exptl. Biol. No.* **6**, 105-127 (1952).
46. Nageotte, J. *Compt. rend. soc. biol.* **68**, 39-42 (1910).
47. Overton, E. *Vierteljahresschr. naturforsch. Ges. Zürich* **40**, 159-201 (1895).
48. Ponder, E. *In* "Handbuch der Protoplasmaforschung" (L. V. Heilbrunn and F. Weber, eds.), Vol. 10, Part 2. Springer, Berlin, 1955.
49. Ritchie, J. M., and Straub, R. W. *J. Physiol. (London)* **136**, 80-97 (1957).
50. Robertson, J. D. *J. Biophys. Biochem. Cytol.* **1**, 271-278 (1955).

51. Robertson, J. D. *In* "Ultrastructure and Chemistry of Neural Tissue" (H. Waelsch, ed.). 'Hoeber-Harper, New York, 1956.
52. Robertson, J. D. *J. Physiol. (London)* **135**, 56-57 (1956).
53. Robertson, J. D. *J. Physiol. (London)* **137**, 8-9P (1957).
54. Robertson, J. D. *J. Physiol. (London)* **137**, 6-8P (1957).
55. Robertson, J. D. *J. Biophys. Biochem. Cytol.* **3**, 1043-1048 (1957).
56. Robertson, J. D. *J. Physiol. (London)* **140**, 58-59P (1957).
57. Robertson, J. D. *J. Appl. Phys.* **28**, 1372 (1957).
58. Robertson, J. D. *J. Physiol. (London)* **142**, 9-11P (1958).
59. Robertson, J. D. *J. Biophys. Biochem. Cytol.* **4**, 39-46 (1958).
60. Robertson, J. D. *J. Biophys. Biochem. Cytol.* **4**, 349-364 (1958).
61. Robertson, J. D. *Proc. Intern. Conf. Electron Microscopy, 4th Conf. Berlin, 1957*, p. 37 (1958).
62. Robertson, J. D. *Biochem. Soc. Symposia (Cambridge, Engl.) No.* **16**, 3-43 (1959).
63. Robertson, J. D. *In* "Tools of Biological Research" (H. J. B. Atkins, ed.), pp. 72-121. Blackwell, Oxford, 1959.
63a. Robertson, J. D. Preliminary Observations on the Ultrastructure of Nodes of Ranvier. *Z. Zellforsch. u. Mikroskop. Anat.* **50**, 553-560 (1959).
64. Robertson, J. D., and Barnicot, N. A. The ultrastructure of human red and white blood cell membranes. In preparation.
65. Roth, L. E. *J. Biophys. Biochem. Cytol.* **2**, Suppl. No. 4, 235-240 (1956).
66. Roth, L. E. *J. Biophys. Biochem. Cytol.* **3**, 816-820 (1957).
67. Schmidt, H. D. *Monthly Microscop. J.* **11**, 200-221 (1884).
68. Schmidt, W. J. *Z. Zellforsch.* **23**, 657-676 (1936).
69. Schmitt, F. O. *Cold Spring Harbor Symposia Quant. Biol.* **4**, 7-12 (1936).
70. Schmitt, F. O. *Exptl. Cell Research Suppl.* **5**, 33-57 (1958).
71. Schmitt, F. O., and Bear, R. S. *Biol. Revs. Cambridge Phil. Soc.* **14**, 27-51 (1939).
72. Schmitt, F. O., Bear, R. S., and Clark, G. L. *Radiology* **25**, 131-151 (1935).
73. Schmitt, F. O., Bear, R. S., and Palmar, K. J. *J. Cellular Comp. Physiol.* **18**, 31-41 (1941).
74. Schmitt, F. O., Bear, R. S., and Ponder, E. *J. Cellular Comp. Physiol.* **9**, 89-92 (1936).
75. Schmitt, F. O., Bear, R. S., and Ponder, E. *J. Cellular Comp. Physiol.* **11**, 309-313 (1938).
76. Ségall, B. *J. anat. et physiol.* **29**, 586-603 (1893).
77. Sjöstrand, F. S. *Experientia* **9**, 68-69 (1953).
78. Sjöstrand, F. S., and Zetterqvist, H. *In* "Electron Microscopy" (F. S. Sjöstrand and J. Rhodin, eds.), p. 150. Academic Press, New York, 1957.

79. Stoeckenius, W. *Proc. Intern. Conf. Electron Microscopy, 4th Conf., Berlin 1957* (Abstr.) p. 204 (1958).
80. Stoeckenhuis, W. *J. Biophys. Biochem. Cytol.* 491-500 (1959).
81. Uzman, B. G., and Nogueira-Graf, G. *J. Biophys. Biochem. Cytol.* **3**, 589-598 (1957).
82. Waugh, D. F. *Ann. N.Y. Acad. Sci.* **50**, 835-853 (1950).
83. Waugh, D. F., and Schmitt, F. O. *Cold Spring Harbor Symposia Quant. Biol.* **8**, 233-241 (1940).
84. Whitear, M. *Experientia* **13**, 287-289 (1957).
85. Williams, P. L., and Wendel-Smith, C. P. *Quant. J. Microscop. Sci.* In press.
86. Young, J. Z. *In* "Essays on Growth and Form" (W. E. le Gros Clark and P. B. Medawar, eds.), pp. 41-93. Oxford Univ. Press, London and New York, 1945.
87. Zetterqvist, H. "The Ultrastructural Organisation of the Columnar Absorbing Cells of the Mouse Intestine," Ph.D. Thesis, Karolinska Institutet. Aktiebolaget Godvil, Stockholm, 1956.

The Heat Production of Nerve

A. V. HILL

University College London, England

The first attempt to measure the heat production of stimulated nerve was recorded by Helmholtz in 1848. The sensitivity available, as we now know, was a thousand times too low. Attempts were continued, all unsuccessful, until 1926, when at last the heat was measured. This was with frogs' medullated nerves. In 1929, the heat production of the nonmedullated limb nerves of spider crabs was measured. It was considerably larger than in medullated nerves. Between 1926 and 1936, many papers were published on the subject; but by 1936, within the limits of the instruments then available, there did not seem to be anything more worth doing, and for twenty years nothing more was done. By 1955, however, the instruments used for measuring the heat production of muscle had been so much improved, particularly with respect to sensitivity and speed, that it seemed likely their application to nerve heat production would yield, possibly novel, almost certainly more accurate results. Both expectations were realized.

Why did people go on trying for eighty years, despite constant failure, to measure the heat production of nerve? Chiefly, in the first instance, in order to settle directly the question of whether the nerve impulse is the sort of physical wave in which the whole of the energy for transmission is impressed on the system at the start. Various properties of nerve, superficially at least, seemed to favor this view, particularly the classic demonstration of its supposed "infatigability." Against it was the existence of an absolute refractory period, during which, after the passage of one impulse, a second one cannot be carried. In this respect, a nerve impulse is unlike any physical wave in which the energy is applied at the start. If it could be shown that heat really was produced all along a nerve during transmission, then the purely physical theory of conduction would be untenable. A distributed relay system of some kind would be required, with energy derived presumably from chemical change.

When the heat was finally measured, it was found to occur in two phases, one early, one late. Much the larger part of it appeared long after the transmission of the impulse. It was clearly a sign of a recharging or recovery process, by which the initial state of the nerve was restored after the electro-chemical and other changes associated with impulse conduction. More interesting, however, was the other part of the heat which seemed to occur during the process of transmission itself—on this most of the research was concentrated. This heat was very small, and the sensitivity required to record it was very high, which made its accurate location in time more difficult. The work of the last few years has been directed mainly to the question of whether the so-called initial heat is really "initial," in the sense that it appears during, and as part of, the elementary process of impulse transmission; and, if so, what is its origin. What in fact is the chemical process that produces it, and how is it involved in the cycle of permeability change that accompanies the impulse, and how is it responsible for its electrical manifestations?

When the limb nerve of a crab at $0°C$ is stimulated by a single shock and transmits a single impulse, there is a total rise of temperature of about $2 \times 10^{-6}°C$. But the quicker instruments now available have revealed the astonishing and quite unprecedented fact that this is only the net result of a diphasic process; the first phase is a rise of temperature of $10 \times 10^{-6}°C$ which seems to occur during the passage of the impulse; the second phase is a fall of temperature of $8 \times 10^{-6}°C$ which lasts for a few tenths of a second afterwards. Neither phase is in any way related to the slower recovery process, which at $0°C$ would take an hour. The phenomenon is best exhibited to the eye by repetitive stimulation of rather low frequency, when the up-and-down deflections are very obvious (Fig. 1). The instruments, of course, are very sensitive and appreciable time lag occurs in the deflection. This can be allowed for by a

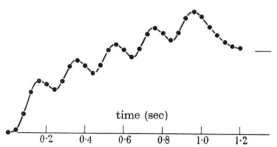

FIG. 1. Heat production and absorption of nonmedullated nerves at 0°C, due to 5 shocks at intervals of 0.20 sec. Mean of eight records. Spots every 0.04 sec. (From A. V. Hill and J. V. Howarth, *Proc. Roy. Soc.* **B149**, 168, 1958.)

numerical analysis; and the heat can be expressed in blocks of 20 msec duration. Figure 2 gives such an analysis of the deflection due to a single shock. It will be noticed that the positive heat production shows a certain dispersion in time, but this is almost certainly due to two facts: (a) that impulses in

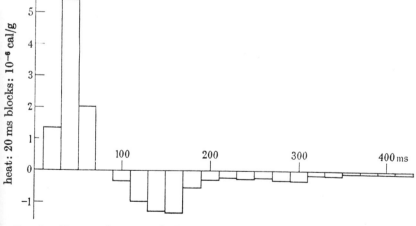

FIG. 2. Heat production and absorption due to single stimulus at 0°C, in 20 msec blocks: units of 10^{-6} cal per gram nerve; time after shock in msec. Mean of five experiments, positive heat 8.8×10^{-6} cal per gram, negative heat 6.8×10^{-6} cal per gram, net heat 2.0×10^{-6} cal per gram. (From B. C. Abbott, A. V. Hill, and J. V. Howarth, *Proc. Roy. Soc.* **B148**, 157, 1958.)

nerve fibers of different diameters travel at different speeds and so get spread out, and (b) that the thermopile contains 100 thermocouples at different distances from the point of stimulation. If these could be accurately allowed for, the positive phase of the heat would probably appear in a single sharp burst during the passage of the impulse. The negative phase, however, is spread out over 300 msec, which is much longer than anything known to be connected with the impulse proper.

These quantities may seem very small, but that depends on how one expresses them. As far as the measurement itself goes, they *are* small; but it seems most likely that the region in which active heat production occurs, at any rate during the impulse itself, is located at the surface membrane of the fibers, not in the main volume of the axoplasm. According to present-day theory, as far as the primary process of the impulse is concerned, the axoplasm serves merely as an electrical conductor, and as a source of K ions to go out, and a sink for Na ions to come in. The surface area of the fibers, in 1 gram of spider crab nerve, is roughly $10^4 cm^2$. If the active surface region were 50 A thick, its volume in 1 gram would be $5 \times 10^{-3} cm^3$, and the positive heat in an impulse, namely, 10^{-5} cal per gram nerve, would become 2×10^{-3} cal per gram surface material. This is not at all a small quantity, as is shown by comparing it with the heat production in a muscle twitch, namely, about 3×10^{-3} cal per gram muscle. So if the primary process in impulse transmission does occur in a thin layer along the fiber surface, the heat production represents a fairly substantial chemical change (comparable with that in a muscle twitch) in the surface material involved.

Various possible sources of the positive and negative heat production have been proposed, none of them satisfactory, or, at any rate, sufficient.

(1). The positive heat is really the Joule's heat of the action current running during the impulse. This can be set aside at once. There is strong evidence that the action current is due solely to Na ions going in during the rising phase of the spike, and K ions coming out during the falling phase. If so, the net thermal effect of the action current, since no external work is done, cannot be other than that of a slight mixing of the internal and external electrolytes, which we will next consider.

(2). The axoplasm and body fluid in crabs are rather strong solutions and when these are mixed, there is a finite positive heat production. Unfortunately, it has not proved possible yet to devise means of measuring the heat of interchange of Na and K ions on solutions analogous to blood (or plasma) and axoplasm. The best, hitherto, that could be done was to use 0.6 M NaCl to represent the outside fluid; 0.6 M KCl to represent the inside fluid. With these, the interchange of Na with an equal amount of K gives a heat production of about 50 cal/mole. The extent of the interchange of Na and K during an impulse is approximately known, from which the thermal effect can be approximately calculated. This could make a substantial contribution to the observed positive heat production, but it has no bearing on the negative phase, which occurs, in any case, after the ionic interchange is over.

(3). After the primary process of inward Na, outward K flow, the ionic movements are slowly reversed by some process which necessarily involves work and probably, therefore, the positive liberation of heat. But this takes a long time and cannot affect the thermal picture of the first few tenths of a second.

(4). During the rising phase of the action potential, the capacitance of the surface membrane of the nerve fiber is discharged. During the falling phase, it is recharged. A charged condenser contains energy, which might be turned into heat during discharge; and recharging might involve an equal and opposite absorption of heat. The capacitance and the potentials are approximately known, and the calculated positive and negative heats are of the right order of size to explain the quantities involved. But this most attractive theory seems to fall down completely over the fact that the time relations are wrong. The action potential of crab nerve at 0°C seems only to last for 20 or 30 msec, while the negative heat continues about ten times as long. If the two phases of the heat production had been completed in 30 msec, the instruments would have been too slow to resolve them at all, and only the net heat would have been observed. In any case, the net heat, about 2×10^{-6} cal per gram nerve, would still remain to be explained.

There is, in fact, another difficulty about the condenser theory, which is much more subtle and about which I am not really quite sure that it is a difficulty. The potential difference between the inside and the outside of a nerve fiber is due to the separation of two solutions with different ionic concentrations. When the solutions are momentarily brought into contact by changes in the permeability of the surface membrane, the first effect is that Na ions move in; then in the falling phase of the action potential, K ions move out. If the energy in the charged condenser could be made to do external work, the nerve might very well cool. If the work were done internally, against the resistance of the nerve fluids, the thermal effect might be nil, or, rather, only that of the mixing of the ions. The system is unlike that of an ordinary condenser charged with electrons; the potential difference is solely due to the separation of the ions. However that may be, the time relations of the recharge of the condenser do not agree with those of the negative phase of the heat.

(5). The *net* heat might be due to the thermal effect of the interchange of ions: that is of the right order of size. But this seems to be negated by the fact that the net heat in an impulse is little affected by temperature; whereas the ionic interchange is greater at a lower temperature, corresponding to the fact that the action current lasts longer, and therefore a greater transport of electricity is involved.

It seems, therefore, that all these attractive possibilities have to be discounted, and we are left with the original hypothesis. This is, that the initial heat is a sign of chemical changes that take place in the surface membrane during the large changes of permeability that occur, and are reversed, during the active phase of the impulse. It is difficult, indeed, to imagine an excitable membrane going through a complete cycle involving a several hundred-fold increase and decrease of permeability, first to Na and then to K ions, and yet behaving as a conservative system without any changes of energy.

Possibly in nerve, as in muscle, a chemical "accumulator" system exists, so that by the end of the permeability cycle, as by the end of a twitch, heat would have been produced. The negative heat appears after the chemical reactions accompanying the permeability changes are already complete, and according to this hypothesis, would be due to some aftereffect of these. In muscle, an endothermic process certainly can occur at an early stage of anaerobic recovery. Here, a whole series of reactions takes place after contraction, and before oxidative recovery has gone far; and during a certain interval, the heat balance may be negative. At present, therefore, I can see no alternative to the hypothesis that the early production and absorption of heat after a stimulus are largely due to chemical reactions associated with, and following, the permeability cycle. Some people may like this hypothesis, some may not; but the facts themselves cannot be explained away. If it is right, then there remains the formidable task for biochemists of finding out what the chemical reactions are which produce the observed, and diphasic, heat production.

Some light may soon, perhaps, be thrown on these chemical reactions in nerve by following up experiments now being made by Aubert and Fessard on the heat production of the electric organ of *Torpedo* during its discharge. This was investigated fifty years ago by Bernstein and Tschermak who found (a result which always semed too simple to be true) that when external electrical work was done by connecting the organ through an external resistance, the heat production was correspondingly diminished. A preliminary reinvestigation of this was begun in 1957 in Arcachon by Abbott, Aubert, and Fessard, and their results were briefly described to the Royal Society last winter. The facts are much more complicated than depicted by Bernstein and Tschermak. The heat production, during and following discharge, goes through a complex cycle of positive and negative phases, which must be a sign of such extensive chemical reactions that they ought to be susceptible to biochemical analysis. Moreover, the organ seems to have properties analogous to those of muscle, which is capable (like an electric motor) of adjusting the amount of energy it uses to the mechanical load imposed on it and to the mechanical work it performs. In the case of the electric organ, the load is electrical, i.e., an external resistance, and the total amount of energy given out by the organ during and after discharge increases with the amount of electrical work. The chemical changes involved in these experiments must have been anaerobic; for the organ was isolated and in so massive a lump of tissue the amount of oxygen available inside by diffusion must have been negligible.

Most of the experiments in the past on nerve heat were made with medullated nerve; and after the recent experiments on crab nerves were finished, it was decided to apply the new methods and instruments to medullated nerve. One object was to see whether in this also the initial heat production is diphasic. Success was not really expected, for the heat in a single impulse in medullated nerve is less than in nonmedullated nerve. Moreover, the processes in medullated nerve are more rapid than in nonmedullated nerve, and the instruments would probably be too slow to separate the two phases, if they existed. These fears were realized. During slow repetitive stimulation, nothing was observed except the usual positive heat. The question, therefore, is unanswered. But one important result was obtained, i.e., the confirmation, by much more rapid instruments, of the former conclusion that the initial heat production is closely associated with the actual passage of the impulse. Owing to the extreme sensitivity required, the instruments could not be very rapid, and appreciable time lag occurred. But this could be eliminated by a numerical analysis; and the heat during a short tetanus, expressed in blocks of 0.2 sec duration, is shown in Fig. 3. The heat production rises immediately to its full rate after the first shock, and drops back again immediately after the last. Although an interval of 0.02 sec at 0°C can be admitted as experimentally possible between the heat and the impulse itself (much less at a higher temperature), the most likely conclusion is that the heat and the impulse are really simultaneous.

The absolute values are of interest. The initial heat in a single impulse in medullated nerve is too small to be measured with accuracy. It can be inferred, however, from such results as those of Fig. 3, and from the observed relation between heat production and stimulation. At 0°C in the nerves of *Rana temporaria* the initial heat is about 0.8 µcal per gram, about

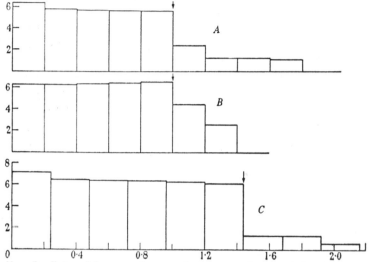

Fig. 3. Rate of heat production during stimulation of frogs' nerve at 0°C, analyzed in blocks every 0.2 sec (*A, B*), or 0.24 sec (*C*). In *A* 51 shocks at 50/sec: in *B*, 26 shocks at 25/sec. The first shock was at time 0.00 sec, the last (shown by arrow) at 1.00 sec (*A, B*), or 1.44 sec (*C*). (From A. V. Hill and J. V. Howarth, *Proc. Roy. Soc.* **B149**, 172, 1958.)

40% of the net heat in crabs' nerves. This justifies an interesting comment on the present view, for which there is very good evidence, that in medullated nerve transmission is saltatory from node to node, not continuous as in nonmedullated nerve. An approximate estimate of the amount of nodal material in 1 gram of nerve is 1.6×10^{-5} gram, so that 0.8 µcal per gram nerve becomes 5×10^{-2} cal per gram nodal material. This is about fifteen times as great as the heat in a single muscle twitch, and it is scarcely conceivable that the nodal material could be more or less infatigable if its metabolism were so high. The same conclusion is arrived at by considering the total area of the nodes, which in 1 gram of nerve may amount to 4 cm^2 (compare this with 10^4 cm^2, 2500 times as much, for the total fiber surface in 1 gram of nonmedullated nerve). This would make the output of energy in an impulse, reckoned per square centimeter of the nodal surface, one thousand times as great as at the fiber surface in a nonmedullated nerve. Finally, during repetitive stimulation at maximal frequency, the rate of initial heat production at room temperature is about 12 µcal g^{-1} sec^{-1}, which reckoned per gram of nodal material comes to 0.75 cal per sec: This is quite an impossible amount.

While admitting, therefore, as experimental fact that the nodes are the sources and sinks of the electric currents by which the impulse is propagated, we cannot conclude that the rest of the material of a fiber is metabolically inert. To do so would be to assume a level of metabolism in the nodal material, or surface, quite beyond the range of what is generally regarded as possible in living material; and that, moreover, in an organ which is notoriously resistant to fatigue.

Aspects of the Molecular Basis of Nervous Activity*

Irwin B. Wilson

Department of Neurology, College of Physicians and Surgeons,
Columbia University, New York

It is true that we are still far from understanding the nerve impulse, yet we have considerable information about it. For example, it is known that the membrane resistance decreases during the impulse, and polarity of the membrane potential reverses (1). There is an influx of sodium ion as the impulse grows; and as it dies away, there is an outflow of an approximately equivalent amount of potassium ion (2–4). The ionic flow is in the direction of the electrochemical gradient, and could therefore be determined by specific passive permeability properties of the membrane if some mechanism exists for bringing about the requisite changes. What is the nature of this change in permeability, and how is it brought about? To a biochemist, it seems certain that chemical changes must be involved, and the occurrence of changes in protein configuration is an attractive theory. The recent studies of A. V. Hill and his associates show that considerable heat is evolved, followed by a somewhat lesser absorption of heat (5).

There are membranes which respond electrically to applied acetylcholine. Indeed this activity of acetylcholine is accepted as basic in the transmission of nerve impulses, although the classic view that acetylcholine is secreted by nerve endings is challenged by Nachmansohn, who proposes that the release and action of acetylcholine is an intracellular process which occurs in both conduction and transmission. The fact is, that there are membranes whose ionic permeability is altered by acetylcholine. Nachmansohn has accumulated considerable evidence

---

* This work was supported in part by the Division of Research Grants and Fellowships of the National Institutes of Health, Grant No. B-573, U. S. Public Health Service, and in part by the National Science Foundation, Grant No. NSF-G-4331.

in support of the theory that acetylcholine is directly involved in the nerve impulse, and has suggested that acetylcholine is a specific agent in changing the ionic permeability of the membrane during the action potential (6, 7).

The existence of membranes which respond with specificity toward acetylcholine suggests the presence of a special acetylcholine receptor. We should, of course, like to know something about its interaction with acetylcholine. It would appear that much of what has been learned about the interaction of acetylcholine and the enzyme acetylcholinesterase might tentatively be assumed to apply also to the receptor. The basis for this argument is that a small molecule such as acetylcholine has but a few features which might contribute to binding with proteins, and since specificity is achieved by the summation of a number of small binding energies, it is plausible to assume that all proteins which interact specifically with acetylcholine must utilize the same binding features.

The activity of acetylcholine is very much greater than β-dimethylamino ethyl acetate, perhaps a thousand times greater. In their reaction with acetylcholinesterase the over-all observations do not differ quite so much. The maximum velocity is about twice as fast for acetylcholine and the Michaelis-Menten constant is about seven times smaller, so that at very low substrate concentration, acetylcholine is hydrolyzed fourteen times faster. When the energies and entropies for the formation of the enzyme-substrate complex are compared, a larger distinction appears (8). In the series of ammonium ions,

$NH_3CH_2CH_2OCOCH_3^+$; β-amino ethyl acetate
$CH_3NH_2CH_2CH_2OCOCH_3^+$; β-methylamino ethyl acetate
$(CH_3)_2NHCH_2CH_2OCOCH_3^+$; β-dimethylamino ethyl acetate
$(CH_3)_3NCH_2CH_2OCOCH_3^+$; acetylcholine

the binding energy decreases, and the entropy increases slowly for the first three members. With acetylcholine however, there is a large decrease in binding energy which is more than compensated by a large increase in the binding entropy. But the large quantitative difference suggests a qualitative difference—it suggests that the enzyme-substrate complex may have a different structure—perhaps one which is looser, or one which is less hydrated. We have here, suggested to us, a kind of difference which might be an explanation of the dissimilarity in the response of the receptor and which would be consistent with the role assigned to it.

Comparison with enzymes suggests that while binding is necessary for activity, a substance might be bound to the receptor which would not evoke activity, i.e., it would not bring about the change in the receptor which leads to depolarization. If, for simplicity, we imagine two states of the receptor—active, and resting, the effect of any substance will depend upon the state with which it can more readily combine. If it is the resting state, it might be called a competitive receptor inhibitor. If it combines more readily with the active state, it could be named a competitive receptor activator. In general, substances which might be expected to react with the active site of the receptor, block nervous activity, some with a decrease in membrane potential and some without affecting the potential.

Activation of the receptor does not require an ester function. Simple quaternary ammonium ions are active, but they are much less active (1/100) than acetylcholine. Interestingly enough, choline is much less active (1/100) than simple quaternary ammonium ions. It would appear that the receptor has a negative specificity for choline. The poorer binding of choline is probably not due to a greater interaction of choline with water, because choline is bound by acetylcholinesterase as well as the simpler quaternary ammonium ions. This especially poor response to choline does not appear to be physiologically valuable with respect to the nerve impulse, because a change by a factor of one hundred would be good enough. Yet this property may be of physiological significance because of the abundance of lecithin and the high concentration of free choline in tissues (the normal concentration of choline in blood is about $10^{-4}\,M$ which would be more than enough to produce response if the activity were equal to that of tetramethyl ammonium ion).

An objection to the view that acetylcholine is involved in conduction, was the lack of effect of even very high concentrations of acetylcholine when applied to axons. Nachmansohn explained this by demonstrating that several quaternary amines (including acetylcholine) do not penetrate into the giant axon of squid, and he extended this observation to include all axons and conducting membranes (9, 10). The general relationship between lipid solubility and permeability offered the possibility that lipid-soluble quaternary ammonium ions might penetrate and be active. Quaternary amines with a long alkyl chain such as dodecyl, trimethyl ammonium ion are biologically active. In fairly low concentration they block conduction in crab and lobster nerve (11). In frog rectus abdominus they produce reversible contracture, even in the presence of very large concentrations of curare (12). Applied to the sartorius (with or without curare) they produce a slow contraction and relaxation (15 seconds) followed by a second and slower cycle (13). Reversible depolarization of the desheathed frog tibialis occurs with as dilute as $10^{-6}\,M$ solution, and it can be competitively antagonized by receptor inhibitors such as eserine (14, 15). Electrical activity of Ranvier nodes of isolated frog sciatic nerve fibers is affected even in $10^{-7}\,M$ concentration (W. D. Dettbarn, unpublished experiments, 1959). Lipid-soluble quaternary amines depolarize conducting membranes in apparently the same manner that simple quaternary ammonium ions depolarize junctions. This is consistent with the role of acetylcholine in conduction and transmission.

Work on the molecular forces of interaction (16, 17) between acetylcholine and acetylcholinesterase, as well as the development of a theory of enzymatic hydrolysis (18) have led to the explanation of the remarkable ability of "alkyl phosphates" to inhibit hydrolytic enzymes irreversibly, and to the synthesis of surprisingly rapid reactivators of the inhibited enzyme (19–21) which in turn proved to be excellent antidotes against these poisons (22–27). Although these poisons inhibit a large number of hydrolytic enzymes, only the inhibition of acetylcholinesterase is important in acute toxicity (28, 29).

The active site of acetylcholinesterase is made up of two principal subsites (Fig. 1). The first is an anionic site (16, 30) which binds and orients the cationic portion of the substrate.

Coulombic forces contribute 2.0 kcal/mole of binding energy (a factor of 30 in the binding constant). In addition all but one methyl group makes a binding contribution on the average of 1.2 kcal/mole (a factor of 7) (*31*). The source of this bind-

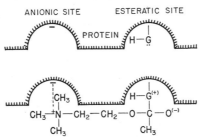

FIG. 1.   The active site of acetylcholinesterase showing the anionic and esteratic subsites and the enzyme substrate complex with acetylcholine.

ing is believed to be the energy of Van der Waal's attraction between the methyl groups and a hydrocarbon portion of the protein in excess of the solvation energies of the uncombined structures. One methyl group projects into the water and so does not contribute to binding. The second subsite is an esteratic site (H—G:) containing an essential acidic group represented by a hydrogen atom and a basic group represented by a pair of electrons. G represents some unknown structure. Binding here is through a covalent bond between the basic group and the electrophilic carbonyl carbon atom.

If we compare ethyl acetate with acetylcholine we note that a quaternary nitrogen function is lacking in the former and therefore acetylcholine should be bound $30 \times 7 \times 7 \approx 1500$ times better than ethyl acetate. In addition, the hydrolytic process is about ten times faster for acetylcholine so that at low substrate concentrations acetylcholine is hydrolyzed some 10^4 times more rapidly. We have here then the method by which enzymes achieve specificity, i.e., by developing a structure which is molecularly complementary to a particular substrate. Such a structure allows the summation of several small interaction energies. The anionic site thus promotes activity toward substrates which contain a suitably located quaternary ammonium function.

During enzymatic hydrolysis of acetylcholine, choline is split out and the basic group of the esteratic site is acetylated. The acetylated enzyme then reacts with water in a few microseconds to regenerate the enzyme and produce acetic acid. The alkyl phosphates are hemisubstrates; instead of an acetyl enzyme a dialkylphosphoryl enzyme is formed but this compound reacts only very slowly with water. However the phosphoryl enzyme reacts more readily with other simple nucleophilic agents notably hydroxylamine. The question arose whether a molecule based on hydroxylamine could be designed so as to exploit the binding features of the enzyme, especially of the anionic site. This compound should have a quaternary function and be bound in such a way that the nucleophilic function (oxygen atom) falls one bond length from, and is directed toward, the phosphorus atom of the phosphoryl enzyme.

It is also important that the molecule be rigid, so that there are very few, and preferably only one, probable configuration. Under these circumstances we should expect a very rapid rate of reactivation of the inhibited enzyme.

The first compound containing a quaternary function, nicotin-hydroxamic acid methiodide (32), was quite successful, and it was then found that the 2-position (33) was much superior. The required molecular rigidity could be obtained by going over to oximes, and pyridine-2-aldoxime methiodide proved to be extremely active. We then had the problem of proving that the remarkable activity of this compound was a consequence of a high degree of molecular complementarity and that the conditions discussed above were fulfilled.

The analysis of this problem was based upon reversible competitive inhibitors (34, 35) especially the dimethyl carbamate of 3-hydroxyphenyl trimethyl ammonium ion (I). By comparison with phenyltrimethyl ammonium ion (II)

(I)   (II)

it was found that the carbamate function makes a contribution of 3.3 kcal (factor of 3000) to binding. An important part of this binding is the formation of a covalent bond between the basic group of the esteratic site and the carbonyl carbon atom. The position of this carbon atom when the compound is bound to the enzyme is therefore a probable position for the phosphorus atom of the phosphoryl enzyme. This molecule is largely planar so that only two pertinent configurations are possible (Fig. 2).

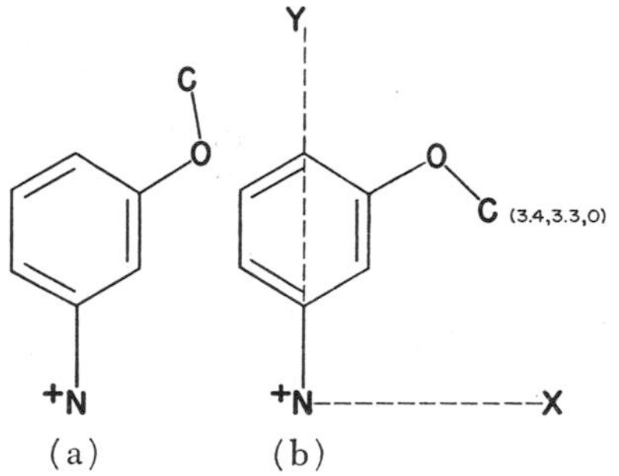

FIG. 2. The two conformations of the dimethyl carbamate of 3-hydroxyphenyl trimethyl ammonium ion. Conformation b is the one which is complementary to the enzyme.

It was possible to show that disposition b (see Fig. 2) is correct, and to locate therefore the position of the phosphorus atom (same position as the carbonyl carbon atom) in the phosphoryl enzyme relative to the coordinate system defined as shown. It is desirable to have a ring in the reactivator molecule because aromatic rings make a large contribution to the binding energy, but more than this, it is essential in order to match our coordinates. The compound pyridine-2-aldoxime methiodide (Zwitter ion) as indicated (Fig. 3) fits the geometry of the phosphoryl enzyme.

Because of resonance, this molecule is planar, so that only two dispositions corresponding to rotation of the side chain by 180° are probable. The second of these dispositions however, is unlikely because of steric repulsion, and we are left with but one configuration. This compound is almost a million times better than hydroxylamine and its great activity derives not only from its functional group but to a very large extent from a very high degree of molecular complementarity.

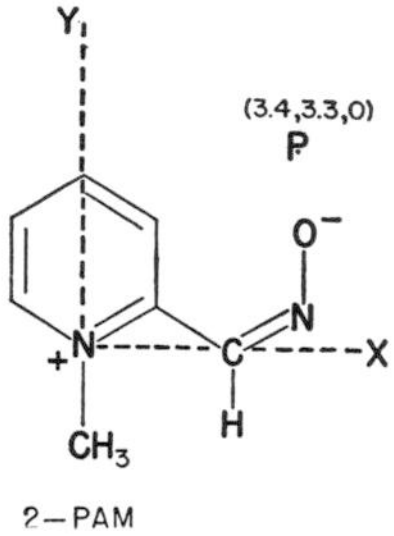

FIG. 3. The molecular complementarity between pyridine-2-aldoxime methiodide and the dialkylphosphoryl enzyme.

We have outlined here some of our results to illustrate how studies of molecular complementarity and chemistry of acetylcholinesterase have provided pertinent information for the understanding of nervous activity.

REFERENCES

1. Cole, K. S., and Curtis, H. J. *J. Gen. Physiol.* **22**, 649 (1939).
2. Hodgkin, A. L. *Biol. Revs. Cambridge Phil. Soc.* **26**, 338 (1951).
3. Rothenberg, M. A. *Biochim. et Biophys. Acta* **4**, 96 (1950).
4. Huxley, A. F. *In* "Ion Transport Across Membranes" (H. T. Clarke and D. Nachmansohn, eds.), p. 23. Academic Press, New York, 1954.
5. Abbott, B. C., Hill, A. V., and Howarth, J. V. *Proc. Roy. Soc.* **B148**, 149 (1958).
6. Nachmansohn, D. *Harvey Lectures Ser.* **47**, 57-99 (1955).
7. Wilson, I. B., and Nachmansohn, D. *In* "Ion Transport Across Membranes" (H. T. Clarke and D. Nachmansohn, eds.), pp. 35-64. Academic Press, New York, 1954.
8. Wilson, I. B., and Cabib, E. *J. Am. Chem. Soc.* **78**, 202 (1956).
9. Rothenberg, M. A., Sprinson, D. B., and Nachmansohn, D. *J. Neurophysiol.* **11**, 111 (1948).
10. Bullock, T. H., Nachmansohn, D., and Rothenberg, M. A. *J. Neurophysiol.* **9**, 9 (1946).
11. Schoffeniels, E., Wilson, I. B., and Nachmansohn, D. *Biochim. et Biophys. Acta* **27**, 629 (1958).
12. Hinterbuchner, L. P., and Wilson, I. B. *Biochim. et Biophys. Acta* **32**, 375 (1959).

13. Hinterbuchner, L. P., and Wilson, I. B. *Biochim. et Biophys. Acta* **31**, 323 (1959).
14. Dettbarn, W. D., Wilson, I. B., and Nachmansohn, D. *Science* **128**, 1275 (1958).
15. Dettbarn, W. D. *Biochim. et Biophys. Acta,* **32**, 381 (1959).
16. Wilson, I. B., and Bergmann, F. *J. Biol. Chem.* **185**, 479 (1950).
17. Bergmann, F., Wilson, I. B., and Nachmansohn, D. *J. Biol. Chem.* **186**, 693 (1950).
18. Wilson, I. B., Bergmann, F., and Nachmansohn, D. *J. Biol. Chem.* **186**, 781 (1950).
19. Wilson, I. B. *J. Biol. Chem.* **190**, 111 (1951).
20. Wilson, I. B., and Ginsburg, S. *Biochim. et Biophys. Acta* **18**, 168 (1955).
21. Davies, D. R., and Green, A. L. *Discussions Faraday Soc.* **20**, (1955).
22. Kewitz, H., and Wilson, I. B. *Arch. Biochem. Biophys.* **60**, 261 (1955).
23. Kewitz, H., Wilson, I. B., and Nachmansohn, D. *Arch. Biochem. Biophys.* **64**, 456 (1956).
24. Wilson, I. B., and Sondheimer, F. *Arch. Biochem. Biophys.* **69**, 468 (1957).
25. Namba, T., and Hiraki, K. *J. Am. Med. Assoc.* **166**, 1834 (1958).
26. Hibbiger, F. *Biochem. J.* **66**, 7P (1957).
27. Wills, J. H., Kunkel, A. M., Brown, R. V., and Groblewski, K. *Science* **125**, 743 (1957).
28. Nachmansohn, D., and Feld, E. A. *J. Biol. Chem.* **171**, 715 (1947).
29. Jones, H. W., Meyer, B. J., and Karel, L. *J. Pharmacol. Exptl. Therap.* **94**, 215 (1948).
30. Adams, D. H., and Whittaker, V. P. *Biochim. et Biophys. Acta* **4**, 543 (1950).
31. Wilson, I. B. *J. Biol. Chem.* **197**, 215 (1952).
32. Wilson, I. B., and Meislich, E. K. *J. Am. Chem. Soc.* **75**, 4628 (1953).
33. Wilson, I. B., and Ginsburg, S. *Arch. Biochem. Biophys.* **54**, 569 (1955).
34. Wilson, I. B., and Quan, C. *Arch. Biochem. Biophys.* **73**, 131 (1958).
35. Wilson, I. B., Ginsburg, S., and Quan, C. *Arch. Biochem. Biophys.* **77**, 286 (1958).

Physiological Effects of Sodium and Guanidinium Ions in the Light of Their Electronic Structure

LEONELLO PAOLONI

Istituto Superiore di Sanità, Rome, Italy

Previous interest in heteroaromatic molecules with one carbon surrounded by three nitrogen atoms (*1*) led us to speculate about the structure of the simplest of such cases, the guanidinium ion. Considerable experimental evidence (*2*) is available showing that the guanidinium ion consists of three equivalent NH_2 groups arranged with a planar trigonal symmetry around the central carbon atom. All the previous explanations of the $C(NH_2)_3^+$ structure have been offered in terms of resonating structures (*3*). It seems to us, however, that a better description can be given in terms of the conventional molecular orbital theory. As shown in Fig. 1, the carbon atom has an empty

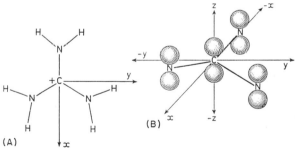

FIG. 1. Electronic structure of the guanidinium ion $C(NH_2)_3^+$. (A) Arrangement of the σ-bonds. (B) Arrangement of the π-orbitals: the orbital on carbon is empty and the orbitals on nitrogen are doubly occupied.

p-orbital where the formal positive charge of the ion is located. Each nitrogen of the NH_2 groups has three planar, trigonally hybridized, atomic orbitals engaged in the σ-bonds with hydrogen and carbon. The lone pair electrons are then on a *p*-orbital, which is involved in a π—π conjugation with the similar atomic orbital on carbon. Altogether, besides the electrons involved in the σ-bonds, there are therefore six electrons, forming a π-like conjugated system through the empty orbital of the central carbon atom.

The molecular diagram representing the distribution of the π-like electrons is shown in Fig. 2. It has been calculated by

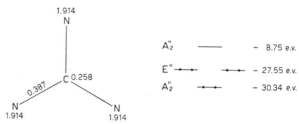

FIG. 2. π-Electron distribution and molecular orbital energy levels for the guanidinium ion.

using the Hückel empirical conventional approach (4).

The proposed structure of guanidinium ion regards it as a triaminocarbonium, that is, an ion of tertiary carbon. We thought therefore it might have some physiological properties analogous to those observed in ions of quaternary nitrogen (alkyl ammonium). While searching the literature for previous observations of such properties, we came across the papers by Lorente de Nò and his co-workers (5). Their results can be summarized as follows.

(1). Guanidinium ion restores the ability to conduct impulses in myelinated fibers (A fibers) of sodium-deficient frog nerve, with practically normal spike duration and speed of conduction.

(2). Substituted guanidinium ions do not have the same ability and, moreover, they render the fibers unexcitable more quickly than a sodium-deficient solution, and retard and reduce the restoring ability of both sodium and guanidinium ions.

(3). Among the few other positive ions able to restore impulse conduction by sodium-deficient nerve fibers, only guanidinium and aminoguanidinium ions maintain the restored conduction for 2 hours or more.

This behavior of guanidinium, remarkably analogous to that of sodium ion, has led us to suggest an explanation for the observations referred to above, and also for the different properties of sodium and potassium ions in the bioelectric processes (6). Na^+ and K^+ differ in fact in the so-called ionic radius and in hydration by different amounts of water (7), but no explanation has been given, as far as we know, in terms of their structure.

The electronic structure of the two free ions is schematically shown in Fig. 3. K^+ has five $3d$ and one $4s$ orbitals available,

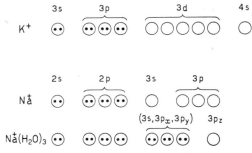

FIG. 3. Valence shell electronic structure of K^+, Na^+ and of the hydrated sodium ion.

which can accommodate from four to six pairs of electrons, and therefore coordinate an equal number of molecules of water; constituting the first water envelope of the K^+ ion, with any one of the symmetries allowed for the configurations d^4 and d^5s.* In the case of Na^+ however, the $3s$- and $3p$-orbitals are empty, making employment of the $3d$ orbitals very unlikely. The analogy of physiological properties with guanidinium ion suggests that the hydrated sodium ion might have a similar trigonal structure, formed by coordination of three molecules of water through the trigonal hybridization of the available $3s$- and $3p$-orbitals. As shown in Fig. 4, each molecule of water would place one of its lone pairs of electrons into the sp-trigonal

---

* Note Added in Proof: Very recent, unpublished calculations by the author indicate that sp^3 and d^2sp^3 configurations are more likely for hydrated K^+ than d^4 and d^5s as proposed above.

orbital of Na^+, thus originating the σ-coordination bonds. The other lone pair of electrons enters a π-conjugation with the central empty p-orbital, giving on the whole, a completely analogous picture to the one seen before for guanidinium.

If the $Na^+ \cdots OH_2$ distance is evaluated by adding the ionic

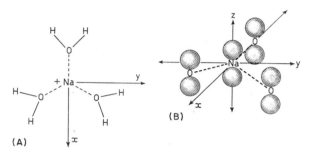

FIG. 4. Electronic structure of the hydrated sodium ion $Na(H_2O)_3^+$. (A) Arrangement of the σ-coordination bonds. (B) Arrangement of the π-coordination orbitals: the orbital on Na^+ is empty and the orbitals on oxygen are doubly occupied.

radius (8) of Na^+, 0.95 A, to the covalent radius of oxygen, 0.65 A, the size of the hydrated sodium ion $Na(H_2O)_3^+$ results in a value about 0.2 A greater than for guanidinium, which has a radius about 2.1 A (2). Besides the possibility of dimensional equivalence, however, the similarity in the nature and shape of the force field generated by the two ions appears of greater importance to us. This circumstance is perhaps better illustrated in Fig. 5, where the π-electron charge distribution of both ions is compared.

The proposed structure of the hydrated sodium ion may explain the observations by Lorente de Nó (5) in a very simple way. Both sodium and guanidinium ion pass through pores of the same size, with the inside surface of the same physical and chemical nature. The alkyl-substituted guanidines however, are stopped at the entrance of the pores and, as they cover the latter with their more or less hydrophobic tails, they hamper the further activity of sodium and guanidinium, retarding their restoring action or making it very difficult.

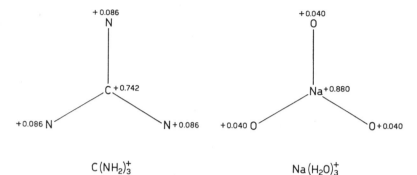

$C(NH_2)_3^+$ $Na(H_2O)_3^+$

Fig. 5. Comparison of the π-electron charges distribution on $C(NH_2)_3^+$ and on $Na(H_2O)_3^+$. This latter is tentatively based on a $Na\cdots O$ distance 1.6 A. (Results to be published.)

ACKNOWLEDGMENT

The encouraging and stimulating discussions with Professor D. Nachmansohn, which resulted in the present communication, are here acknowledged with thanks.

REFERENCES

1. Paoloni, L. *Gazz. chim. ital.* **84**, 735 (1954); **87**, 313 (1957); Dewar, M. J. S., and Paoloni, L. *Trans. Faraday Soc.* **53**, 261 (1957).
2. Angell, C. L., Sheppard, N., Yamaguchi, A., Shimanouchi, T., Miyazawa, T., and Mizushima, S. *Trans. Faraday Soc.* **53**, 589 (1957); Curtis, R. M., and Pasternak, R. A. *Acta Cryst.* **8**, 675 (1955); Bryden, J. H., Burkardt, L. A., Hughes, E. W., and Donohue, J. *Acta Cryst.* **9**, 573 (1956).
3. Pauling, L. "The Nature of the Chemical Bond," p. 213. Comstock, Ithaca, New York, 1948; see also Angell *et al.* (2).
4. Paoloni, L. *Gazz. chim. ital.* **89**, 957 (1959).
5. Larramendi, L. M. H., Lorente de Nó, R., and Vidal, F. *Nature* **178**, 316 (1956); Lorente de Nó, R., Vidal, F., and Larramendi, L. M. H. *Nature* **179**, 737 (1957).
6. Huxley, A. F. *In* "Ion Transport Across Membranes" (H. T. Clarke and D. Nachmansohn, eds.), p. 23. Academic Press, New York, 1954.
7. Journet, G., and Vadon, J. *Bull. soc. chim. France* **1955**, 593; Stokes, R., and Robinson, R. A. *J. Am. Chem. Soc.* **70**, 1870 (1948); Szent-Györgyi, A. "Bioenergetics," p. 80. Academic Press, New York, 1957.
8. Pauling, L. "The Nature of the Chemical Bond," pp. 164, 346. Comstock, Ithaca, New York, 1948.